SEX, FERTILITY AND THE CATHOLIC

ALBA HOUSE
a division of
St. Paul Publications
Staten Island, N.Y.

sex, fertility & the catholic

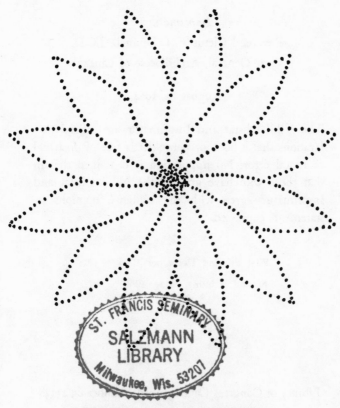

don & helen kanabay

Nihil Obstat:

Reverend Joseph Mangan, S.J.

Imprimatur:

Reverend Cletus F. O'Donnell, J.C.D.

Vicar General, Archdiocese of Chicago

August 12, 1964

The Nihil Obstat and Imprimatur are official declarations that a book or pamphlet is free of doctrinal or moral error. No implication is contained therein that those who have granted the Nihil Obstat and Imprimatur agree with the contents, opinions or statements expressed.

First Printing December 1965

Second Printing, May 1966

This book is dedicated,
With love,
To our children
And yours.

TABLE OF CONTENTS

INTRODUCTION

Why books need introductions is a question many people rightly ask. But evidently they are needed—the introductions, that is, no less than the people—otherwise, they would not continue.

Amid the Introduction-Writers, Introduction No. B4793 is the most popular (and also the easiest one to write). It begins: "There is a great need for this book. If ever something was needed, this book was needed."

On the other hand, Introduction No. L5988 takes the tack of let-confusion-reign-supreme. It says nothing about the book to come, but puts into print something that the Introducer thought about some time. "Horticultural enthusiasm is a talent I have always longed for, and I am happy to take this occasion of writing an Introduction for *A Lively Look at Fertility,* or whatever the title of the book is that I am introducing, so that I can hope that you, too, will be a horticultural enthusiast."

But the Introduction that fits in the present instance is Number A1111: written by the authors themselves without a conscious effort on their part to make it such. Here we have the frank, relaxed, genuinely solid reason for the existence of

9

Sex, Fertility and the Catholic. When the Kanabays requested me to be the Introducer, I was astounded by the fittingness of the words and thoughts they expressed. I do not think that a stranger to the genesis of this book could improve on the convictions from the hearts of those who brought it forth:

"There has been a great deal of arrant nonsense published in the popular and religious press in recent months on the Church's position on birth control, written by ostensibly Catholic authors—wild-eyed liberals who want to determine moral teaching by popular vote—promulgating their own weird brand of theology, and attempting to create the impression that the rank and file of the Catholic clergy and laity are diametrically opposed to the Church's teaching.

"The fact that this group has been able to make itself heard—and believed—in even the so-called Catholic press indicates to us the need for a strong rebuttal that will effectively reach the same audience.

"Just as a priest is better suited than a doctor to speak on sex education of children, because it is character education imbued with spiritual values, so we believe that laymen and laywomen are best suited to speak to other husbands and wives on the matter of periodic continence in marriage. It was on the basis of this belief that we wrote this book.

"The trouble with most books on rhythm is that they either bore the reader or scare him away. In our attempt to reach a large audience with our message—that the rhythm method is not only an efficient means of controlling births, but is also an efficacious means to sanctity in Christian marriage—we have employed an approach that is, to say the least, unorthodox, and is liable to objection from some quarters that the authors have been 'indelicate.'

"But on the other hand we believe that desperate circumstances require unusual remedies, and that the average couple attempting to practice rhythm is fast approaching the point of desperation. That's our windup. Here comes the pitch."

And you, gentle reader, will find that pitch directly after this Introduction. May I as Official Introducer emphasize that this book does *not* say: "practice rhythm!" It does say: "If you feel that rhythm fits your marriage, read this."

We all have heard the colloquial comment that if enough mud is thrown, some of it is bound to stick. Hardly any topic connected with marriage morality has had more ridicule directed at it than rhythm—even though some of this has been occasioned by well-intentioned but objectively erroneous advocacy of rhythm. On the friendly side there has been the good-humored joshing, especially when some couples have vaunted their familial superiority of six boys and girls (and proud of them all!)—"and we got them all by using rhythm!"

But the situation only too often is far, far removed from something that can be passed off in light-hearted banter. Tragedy abounds, too: anguish of conscience, apparently insurmountable problems represented by opposing pressures, all of which seem to be inevitable in their relentlessness.

At a Catholic forum the speaker had been opting for complete freedom for married couples to make up their own minds about marriage morality, so that "they would not be subjected to the intolerable tensions that result when sexual intercourse has been forbidden because of the injunctions of a celibate cleric." It was a husband and wife who exclaimed in despair and disappointment: "When will we hear something about self-control and self-sacrifice for the love of God and for the love of each other?"

If, on the one hand, self-styled progressive thinkers have wiped away with a word the eternal laws of living supported by the "conservatives," it may not be amiss to point out here that this book blasts the error of neglecting the unfathomable meaning of sex in marriage in the name of catering to the imperiousness of sex. "Celibate clerics" have reacted in this extreme, too.

This "celibate cleric" joyfully welcomes the Kanabays with their message. If their book, no less than this introduction, will receive criticism for being "negative," this will be the supreme compliment of being classed with the "negative" thinking of the divine Celibate who taught with no compromise, "Thou shalt not commit adultery," just as He taught, "Thou shalt love the Lord thy God with thy whole heart, thy whole body and thy whole soul, and thy neighbor as thyself."

Rev. Francis L. Filas, S.J.

Chairman, Department of Theology
Loyola University, Chicago, Illinois

AUTHORS' PREFACE

At the close of a social gathering one night last year, one attractive young matron earned the enmity of the other females in the room, particularly those in varying stages of pregnancy, with the remark:

"I think it's marvelous to be pregnant. I think everyone should be pregnant—but me."

This year, to the immense and un-Christian satisfaction of all who happened to be within hearing on that fateful night, that woman is pregnant, and thus finds herself numbered, against the odds, among the decreasing percentage of Catholic women who this year will give birth to a baby.

She has done her part—albeit small, but obviously the most she could do in any one year—in contributing to the population increase in the United States; which, in spite of the steady decrease in the national birth rate during the past several years, is expected to amount to a twenty per cent increase in gross population from 1960 to 1970.

The study of statistics can be a fascinating and frustrating experience. Demographers base their predictions, not unlike the method used by veteran horse players, on past performance; and find themselves collecting win money an equally infinitesimal part of the time.

What the statisticians and prognosticators fail to take into account is the total and utter unpredictability of the American woman, and any man who attempts to predict anything at all about her—much less her fertility rate, of all things!—is playing birthrate roulette with loaded ovaries.

But predict they do, and every ten years or so they find they are well above, or far below, the actual performance and production of the American wife and mother.

And, like racetrack devotees, they proclaim they would have been right, if it just hadn't been for that other horse, (or intangible and unaccountable fact or attitude), that made them lose the race.

Why does a woman have a baby? For a variety of reasons. From instinct, or from a sense of duty. For love, or for social position.

And by accident.

We are not going to make any predictions as to how many women are going to have how many babies, or for which of the above reasons, during the next ten or twenty years.

If one looks at the records of past performance, however, one will not be surprised to discover that the Catholic birthrate in this country is about forty per cent higher than the national average.

There are multitudinous reasons why this should be so. Some will say it is because we practice family limitation, if at all, by the rhythm method, and that this faster growth is the result of accidental conception.

Catholic moralists will say it is because we are trained to believe that the primary purpose of marriage is the procreation and education of children, and thus our tendency is to practice family limitation, if at all, later in married life than our non-Catholic neighbors.

It is quite possible both of them would be right. In any

event, the Catholic population has increased from about twenty per cent of the U. S. total in 1952 to about twenty-four per cent in 1964.

Since Catholics are included in the national average, it might be interesting to look at the picture from a different angle, that of registered church membership. Between 1952 and 1961, Catholics increased about fifty per cent—a growth rate higher than the Catholic birth rate!—and Protestants, twenty per cent. One disturbing fact noted here is that Americans not registered in any church increased fifteen per cent.

We find ourselves more concerned about a fifteen per cent increase in apathy, agnosticism and atheism than we are about a fifty per cent increase in the strength of the Church.

If the present fertility rates of Catholics and non-Catholics hold steady until 1980—and we doubt that they will—the Catholic population will increase by about sixty-five per cent. This would amount to about twenty-eight per cent of the population, and contrary to any anti-Catholic feeling that may still exist, this is not necessarily bad.

On the other hand, most Catholics are aware of the increasing problems and pressures in our school system. In the past twenty-five years, our grade and high school enroll-ment has more than doubled, as compared to an increase in the public school system of something over fifty per cent.

Many Catholic educators are wondering whether we can build schools fast enough. Most doubt it.

The Rev. John L. Thomas, S.J., in an address at Purdue University in November of 1962, stated:

"We agree with the Protestants, for example, on the basic need of responsible parenthood whereby marriage is seen as a total creative process, with the obligation of educating the child and preparing him for a mature adult life. This demands the setting up by the individual couple, of a community of love in which, if God blesses them with a child, it is not only procreated but reared properly."

This statement may come as quite a surprise to those who have derived from their upbringing the belief that the diaper pail is the road to sanctity. It certainly can be, as can any particular state of life which God sends to us. But—and this is the important distinction—it doesn't *have* to be, simply because we are Catholic.

Despite the dire forebodings of the "standing room-and-starvation" demographers, the first concern of the average husband and wife is the welfare of their own family—although they would be justified in taking into account the Family of Man—and the number of children they can properly rear.

There are undoubtedly a great number of good Catholics, with a small number of children, who have been made to feel they were "second class" Catholics, simply because they did not have as many children as those whose families are exhibited in the magazine sections of the Sunday newspapers on Easter morning.

The Rev. John A. O'Brien, research professor of theology at the University of Notre Dame, electrified the Catholic community with his article in *Ave Maria* in January of 1963, in which he warned that overpopulation poses a threat to the world "second only to the danger of nuclear war."

Father O'Brien concludes that conceptions and births must be regulated "by moral methods."

At this time, there is only one method of birth control that is morally acceptable to all.

That method is rhythm.

This is just as true today as it was fifty years ago, and it will be true fifty or a hundred years from now, notwithstanding the newspapers and magazines—including so-called "Catholic" magazines—which darkly hint that the Catholic Church is about to reverse its position on contraception and direct sterilization, temporary or permanent.

The Church does not object to birth control, family planning or responsible parenthood. It merely condemns those methods of arriving at this result which are contrary to the natural law.

The authors are among those who have decided, for the present time, subject to the teaching authority of the Church, our collective and mutual consciences, and the Will of God, to practice the rhythm method of birth control.

That we have been successful in its practice, in spite of a variable menstrual cycle ranging from twenty-six to thirty-six days, is not a tribute to ourselves by any means. It is a tribute to the efficacy of the rhythm method, when conscientiously and intelligently applied.

Ironically, this raucous hue and cry about the Church embracing contraception—which would not be unlike the Virgin Mary embracing the Serpent—comes at a time when science is perfecting methods to narrow the period of continence to limits unquestionably palatable even to those least interested in self-discipline.

The time is not far away when such abstinence will be limited to four or five days, with absolute safety and confidence. The simplicity and esthetic attraction of the rhythm method of birth control, as stated by the English priest and economist, Fr. McCormack, "will make contraception as old-fashioned as the Model-T Ford."

Our book is directed primarily to those who want to use

rhythm, and are willing to learn; to those who have tried rhythm, have been unable to make it work, and have continued to have more children than they are able to cope with; and to those Catholics who, because of their failures in the application of the rhythm method, have lamentably put the Church aside, being convinced that they must limit their families, and having no confidence in the rhythm method.

Advocates of the "new theology of personhood" forget the fact that marriage is not an end in itself, justifying any and all means to preserve itself. Marriage is a means to an end: ultimate union with the One who said, "I have come to bring a sword, not peace ... and a man's enemies will be those of his own household."

For those who are led to a road away from Christ by their contraceptive-minded mates, the response must be: "We have come this far together, but if you follow that path, you go alone."

The authors take no position on the question of whether a large family is better than a small family, or vice versa. We concur with this statement by the Rev. D. F. Miller, C.SS.R., editor of the Redemptorist magazine *Liguorian*:

"Large families have intrinsic values, but no priest, no relative, no doctor, no friend, has any right to dictate to married people in general as to how large a family they should have. Each married couple has its own problems, its own circumstances, its own freedom and responsibility. They have to weigh all the factors involved and should be respected for the decisions they make under God."

We do not say you *should* practice rhythm. We do say, if you make this determination, as we have, that you have a right to make rhythm work.

Don and Helen Kanabay

CHAPTER 1

RHYTHM FOR FUN AND PROFIT

Let us assume you know enough about sex to understand that babies are made by an act of sexual union between a man and a woman, in cooperation with God.

Further, without going into the scientific details at this point, that if sexual intercourse is enjoyed at a particular time of the month, one of those millions of muscular male sperm will swim upstream and fight its way to the arms of the passive and fertile female egg, and bingo! You're a father. Or a mother.

We hope you understand this. It will save all of us a lot of trouble later.

We are also going to assume you know what you like, and that what you like will either make you fat or pregnant. Or, in the latter case, both. Unless you happen to be a man, in which case your wife will probably get big enough for both of you.

We are going to assume that you are married, or about to be married; that you wish to plan your family, within the limits of God's design; and that within the limitations of your conscience and the laws of the Church, you want to use the rhythm method.

You must first realize that rhythm, like copulation, cannot be practiced by one person. One male and one female—both willing, in either instance, for optimum results—are required.

For that reason, we recommend that *both* of you read this book. If you are already blessed with children, and they are making too much noise for you to concentrate, that is all the more reason for your undivided attention.

We won't suggest waiting until the children go to bed. You'll be too exhausted, emotionally and physically, by then. Try reading it in the bathroom, with the door locked. This should be good for at least ten minutes at a time, until you start wondering why the three-year-old is screaming, or what that terrible pounding is.

If you are one of these strong-nerved people who wants to have a lot of children, you should read this book anyway. You may change your mind after the third or fourth child, and that is no time to start wondering what to do.

On the other hand, if you still want a baker's dozen or so, you haven't lost anything by becoming informed. And you can prove to your smaller-familied friends that you know as much as they do, and it simply happens to be a matter of choice with you.

We recently overheard the following conversation in a funeral home:

Woman: "I have nine children."

Man: "Nine children? I've got three, and that's enough for me."

Woman: "When I had three children, that was enough for me, too. But I still have nine."

We realize that a funeral parlor was a strange place to hear that conversation. That hasn't got anything to do with it. That happens to be where we heard it, and we just thought we'd mention it.

Incidentally, a man of our acquaintance with eight or nine children once surprised us with the revelation that he was not Catholic. We had, of course, assumed he was. To put it in his words: "No, just a careless Protestant."

It seems that every large family is automatically suspected of being Catholic, even by other Catholics, or maybe especially by other Catholics.

We haven't the faintest idea whether the woman in the funeral home was Catholic, but we rather suspect she was.

See what we mean?

Another non-Catholic friend, when his wife was carrying their fourth unplanned child, told us about their system of birth control. If his wife told him to use a contraceptive, he used a contraceptive. If she "thought" she was safe, he didn't use a contraceptive. Things obviously weren't working out too well.

We attempted to advise him on the subject of rhythm. "I'm not interested," he said, figuratively yawning. "That's up to her to figure out."

The last we heard, they were expecting number five.

We must emphasize that the practice of rhythm is *not* the woman's sole responsibility. Both husband and wife—again, as with the sexual act itself—must take an active part in understanding it, interpreting it, and helping one another in its practice.

We believe that most men would become extremely resentful if it were entirely up to their wives to say, "Yes, we can," or "No, we can't." It is a joint and mutual responsibility.

This is particularly true in view of the fact that most women are psychologically and emotionally incapable of reading their own charts. One of the major causes for failure of the rhythm system is that the husband leaves it in his wife's discretion and control; whereas a man who is intelligent, informed and displays qualities of leadership—that is to say, the average man—will not only assist his wife in keeping the records and interpreting them, but will assume the position of primacy in this regard.

We do not believe that unplanned pregnancies are limited to Catholic women; and an increasing number of non-Catholics are showing rising interest in rhythm as the only moral method of spacing their children.

In our own circle, we have spoken to several non-Catholic brides-to-be who have indicated they do not intend to use contraceptives in their marriage.

We seem to be giving a doubly incorrect impression here, that all of our friends are non-Catholic, and that all we talk about is birth control. As to the latter, the subject just seems to crop up occasionally—after all, we are writing a book— and our friendly relations with non-Catholics are all a part of the new ecumenical spirit.

Just the other day, a Catholic woman of our acquaintance said to your female author, "I'll have another one if you will."

(Your male author still contends she was talking about martinis, not babies).

Rhythm has a purpose, a premise and a precept.

The purpose is threefold:

    1. Remain in a state of grace.

    2. Enjoy your marital rights.

    3. Don't get pregnant.

The premise:

Rhythm can be better, safer and more efficient than any other form of birth control short of castration.

The precept:

As with any other popular national sport, its rules are precise. It permits no deviation because of state of intoxication or momentary passion. One strike and you're out. Play ball according to the rules, and you'll have your "innings."

Rhythm, not unlike sexual union itself, can be fairly easy at times, and at other times somewhat difficult. During periods of abstinence, you may find your "bell" ringing. There are methods by which to quiet this unseemly cry for attention by your genitals, which will be discussed in a later chapter.

There are, as some see it, two objections to the practice of rhythm:

1. It's too much bother.

2. It doesn't work.

It is true that rhythm takes time and attention. So does love between a man and a woman. Carelessness and thoughtlessness have no place in a marriage, nor in any of its aspects: the education of children, the expression of sexual love, or the development of true spiritual love of two human beings, united by God's grace, and blessed, in His infinite wisdom, with the product of that love.

As you read this book, remember this:

Rhythm works. But, like contraception, it is terribly **unforgiving** of any carelessness, ignorance or neglect.

CHAPTER 2

DOCTORS CAN BE DANGEROUS

There is a fallacy commonly existent in the mind of the average layman that doctors know more about sex than people do.

They don't. Anatomy, yes. Sex, no.

Or, if they are aware of any super-secret sexual knowledge, they aren't telling anyone what they know, because they intend to write an article about it some day for the American Medical Association, or maybe Dr. Hudson's Secret Journal.

Whatever it is, they've been passing out an awful lot of bad information.

Let us take, for example, Mrs. Basal Dip-an-peak. She approaches her doctor, filled with confidence in his abilities— after all, those shots he gave little Jimmy did wonders for him—gripping her thermometer in one hand and her charts in the other.

"Doctor," she says, "I'm having a little trouble reading these. I wonder if you could help me."

The doctor, of course, wears glasses, which gives him that

intelligent look; and suffers from hemorrhoids, which give him that pained expression.

He grunts, pauses between the patients in Room 3 and Room 5—she's in Room 4—and without closing the door, and without looking at the charts, says loudly, so it seems that everyone in the reception room can hear him:

"Five days after your period stops."

And he is on his way, bandages flying, hypodermic glistening, issuing terse commands to his squad of nurses.

So Mrs. Dip-an-peak skulks out through the reception room, crumpling her charts into her purse, absolutely sure that everyone knows why she was seeing the doctor, and continues to have relations with her husband for five days after the end of her period, because that's what the doctor said, and if she gets pregnant the second month it just proves that rhythm doesn't work and the Church is being unreasonable.

What the doctor hasn't taken time to tell her is that her period may stop five days after onset, or four days, or six days. And if it's five days, and she continues to have sexual relations with her husband for another five days, and she is going to have a twenty-seven day period, that's it.

She won't have to worry about getting pregnant for the next nine months.

Or let us consider Mrs. Bluetape. She withdraws from her purse a cylindrical, pristine object called a Fertility Testor.

"Doctor, will you show me how to use this?" she asks.

This time the doctor snorts. "Don't know what they're thinking of these days." He opens a drawer and picks up a fascinating plastic model of the female genital organs, three-dimensional, transparent, and in living color.

"Look," he sneers, "you're going to go right past the cervix with that thing." He traces the path from the vaginal opening with his sterile finger.

"It won't work," he says emphatically.

At this point, a terribly efficient nurse—have you ever known one that wasn't?—pokes her head into the room, pretends you aren't there, and says, "What should I do about Room 7?" And the doctor says, "Give him three cc." (Nurses *never* refer to patients by name in the presence of others; just room numbers).

Mrs. Bluetape is cowed by the sight of her organs being displayed in the doctor's hand, like an object d'art, and is embarrassed because she knows the nurse is irritated that she is taking so much of Doctor's time for something so unimportant as conception regulation.

Abashed and intimidated, Mrs. Bluetape quickly sneaks the testor back into her purse. She wonders if the pharmacist has cheated her.

"Well, I saw this ad," she begins—

The doctor drops the colorful replica back into the drawer, waves his hand airily to show the matter is settled, and there are no hard feelings, even if her ignorance is appalling, and says:

"Why don't we fit you with a diaphragm?"

And since he knows she's Catholic, he thus violates her trust in him as "family doctor," as he makes it clear that he has nothing but contempt for her religious convictions.

It does help if your doctor is Catholic. A non-Catholic doctor, understandably, has little or no interest in rhythm. (You'd think he would, just scientifically—after all, it was discovered by doctors—but he doesn't).

But even a Catholic doctor has his limitations. He, like his non-Catholic brothers in the profession, is unbelievably busy

treating colds, flu, diabetes and overweight. He is perform-
ing appendectomies, suturing gaping wounds, and setting
broken bones. He is trying to keep up with the latest medical
news on miracle drugs.

And he is delivering babies.

Oh, boy, is he delivering babies!

We know why he's delivering babies, don't we? Because
he hasn't had the time or interest to help you read your
charts, or show you how to find your cervix.

Father Filas, our Introducer, in his record, "Sex Education
of Children," discusses the idea that many people have about
calling on a doctor in the area of sex education. He makes
his point well by asking, "Call in a doctor? Well, who's sick?"

There unfortunately exist a certain number of doctors who
continue to insist that the whole theory of rhythm is faulty.
These physicians are apparently not cognizant that in laboratories throughout the world exciting research is going
forward on the scientifically recognized premise of cyclic
rhythm: that ovulation precedes menstruation within a specific
range of days, just as day precedes night within a specific
range of hours.

The female hormone system displays such a dramatic array
of fireworks just prior to and at the time of ovulation that
it is incomprehensible that there should still exist members
of the medical profession who deny this elementary truth.

But they do exist—in small numbers, we hope—and the
disconcerting possibility also exists that one of these men
may be your family doctor.

We do not presume to say that some doctors cannot be
helpful in the area of assisting in the interpretation of your
charts, and in helping you to apply whatever method of

rhythm you are using. If you can find one of them, more power to you.

A good place to look is among the membership of your local chapter of the Catholic Physicians' Guilds. More about these men in Chapter Ten. For the moment, let us simply thank God that there are conscientious professional men who are dedicated to practicing their arts while never forgetting their responsibilities as Catholics.

We do say, loudly, do not assume that your doctor, by virtue of his medical education and practice, can substitute for your own intellect in applying the formulae.

So don't look to your friendly family doctor for all the answers. He hasn't the time, it isn't his job, and he certainly hasn't the interest in your birth control problems that you have.

Any husband and wife who keep accurate records, and learn to interpret them, will know more about rhythm than their doctor does.

Learn what you're doing, use reasonable common sense and prudence, and you can continue, month after month after month, to enjoy the benefits of what your grandmothers used to refer to as "the Curse."

CHAPTER 3

ABSTINENCE MAKES
THE HEART GROW FONDER

In the last chapter, while we were waiting in the doctor's reception room, browsing through the book rack, we came across a booklet entitled, *"A Doctor's Marital Guide for Patients."*

Investigation revealed there were two editions available: the "regular" and the "rhythm." We suppose this means that people who practice rhythm are "irregular" or "non-regular," but at least they aren't calling it the "Catholic edition" any more, which would indicate to us that the publishers realize that Catholics aren't the only people who have moral qualms about contraception.

Having a curiosity in the methods used by "regular" people to practice birth control, we purchased both editions, which left the doctor somewhat bewildered—as a matter of fact, he actually tried to talk us out of buying both editions, for some reason unknown to us—and we were amused to discover that the various methods of contraception seemed to involve more confusion, preparation and detail than the practice of rhythm.

The male half of this writing team was particularly infuriated with a discussion of the spermatoxin: "It has long been know that an injection of her husband's sperm can make a woman develop antibodies against that sperm. Thus her body will combat the sperm after intercourse, instead of welcoming it."

This strikes us as a terrible blow to the male ego, and we cannot conceive that any red-blooded husband would tolerate such insolence.

The nastiest thing the "regular" edition had to say about rhythm was: "Many women simply do not do the arithmetic carefully enough, and many ardent husbands will not always be thwarted by a calendar and pencil."

If said husband were wielding said pencil, and were superintendent in charge of stop-and-go, the weight of responsibility might well quash untimely ardor.

Further on, they admit that ". . . the rhythm method offers a satisfactory degree of protection against unwanted pregnancy to rigorously selected and carefully instructed wives who, with their husbands, are intelligent and strongly motivated."

They have made the very point that we wish to make: that the successful practice of rhythm should be, and is, a status symbol. It marks the thoughtful, intelligent, successful and practical Catholic.

It is a pity that so many people look upon abstinence merely as a means of avoiding conception. Like the man who told us he and his wife "grow apart during abstinence," they think of it as a negative factor in their marriage—an absence, a zero—and overlook the fact that it is a "plus," rather than a "minus" action, performed jointly by husband and wife, together, toward a positive good in their marriage.

Since motivation is a prime factor in the successful practice of rhythm, we'd like to digress for a moment on the subject of Catholic abstinence, and quote from Cardinal Suenens' book, *Love and Control*,[1] where he discusses the traditional Jewish ideal:

"Each month, beginning with the start of the menstrual period, the couple are obliged not to make love for a certain number of days. This initial obligation to 'separateness' offers many benefits to health as well as psychological and moral advantages: it brings the couple a time of physical rest; revives in them a new feeling of attraction, a reagent against the danger of satiety, a constant threat, with its consequent marital lassitude; and finally, proves how necessary it is to be able to control the demands of the flesh."

Cardinal Suenens continues: "The only reason for citing this position here is to show that, among one class of people at least, periodic continence is not considered an unattainable ideal. We can overlook the specifically Jewish obligation to a periodic but complete separation, and still see that there are advantages in a reasonable use of periodic continence, for knowledge's sake, which may include every normal physical intimacy without ending in the marriage act's usual terminal reflex."

The Rev. William Wylie, a theologian of the Anglican Church, writing in *Ramparts* (Jan. 1964), a lay magazine, states that Catholic couples who do not use contraceptives have no choice but abstinence, and that such abstinence is unnatural and "deprives marriage of an essential element . . .

---

1 Newman Press, 1964, p. 81.

for in man passion can turn into devoted and self-sacrificing love."

Cardinal Suenens, however, says "Fidelity comes from grace, not passion." And we would ask how love can be self-sacrificing, if it never knows sacrifice, but only gratification.

Those who rend their garments on the subject of rhythm continue to emphasize a negative view toward abstinence, and deny the positive good that can be added to marriage by the development of a control that will deepen the individual's ability to love. Not every individual, of course, has an equal capability to love. The varying degrees of this capability ascend from zero to ninety-nine per cent. (No one is perfect.) But just as any capability can be improved, so an individual's love capacity can be developed.

As Bishop Fulton J. Sheen has said, in discussing the difference between sex and love: "Love is an act of the will." We constantly hear the objection to rhythm that it is "making love by the calendar," and that it destroys spontaneity. Many modern men and women are trying frantically to wring something out of sex which doesn't exist in nature—the bluebird of continuous titillation.

Anyone who knows what constitutes a good marriage knows that by its nature it will keep getting better. Spontaneity is the kindergarten stage, and its role lessens with the maturing (not aging) of the marriage. Those who rely on spontaneity are cheating themselves and showing a shortsightedness that could be disastrous. They are not building anything between themselves, but relying upon a chemistry that can exist between total strangers (and frequently does) to guide their most personal physical intimacy.

When one insists on spontaneity, it is because a personal

impulse of sexual desire has asserted itself. This is a selfish application, the immediate purpose of which is definitely self-gratification, as opposed to a mutual planning, the prime purpose of which is a mutual goal and a mutual satisfaction.

If one relies upon spontaneity, one does not develop the "art." The willed desire is completely missing. One is a toy of fate regarding one's love life, and if the spontaneity mechanism goes awry, because of some outside influence, one is left without technique. (The proponents of spontaneity have no idea of what they're missing in the development of technique).

Even in the corny seduction movies, the "spontaneity" is usually well planned—i.e., the soft lights and romantic music —and we often wonder how many married couples are able to enjoy the "spontaneity" on which they place so much emphasis with the husband away at work, or the wife fixing dinner, or the children needing help with their homework, or when any of the thousand details arise which call for attention in the management and operation of home and family.

But still we meet couples who complain that abstinence deprives them of spontaneity, as if that is the one thing that is stopping them from achieving married bliss.

There has been a great deal of arrant nonsense published on the position of the Catholic Church and the defects, so-called, in the rhythm system of birth control. The Readers' Digest, the Saturday Evening Post, popular women's magazines and Sunday supplements have publicized unrealistic, slanted and ridiculous viewpoints that tend to make Catholics hide in doorways when their non-Catholic friends approach down the street.

Sensation-seeking authors, ostensibly Catholic, peddle their own weird brand of theology, and attempt to create the impression that the rank and file of the Catholic clergy and laity are diametrically opposed to the Church's position on birth control.

An example of this type of writing appeared in the *Saturday Evening Post* (Apr. 4, 1964), in an article by Rosemary Ruether entitled, *"A Catholic Mother Tells: 'Why I Believe in Birth Control.'"*

Most Catholic mothers, of course, believe in family planning and responsible parenthood. It is merely the method of control that is in dispute.

We will overleap Mrs. Ruether's transgression into the field of theology—she says "rhythm is theologically meaningless." Let us also ignore the cliché of the poor family, with the sick mother and far too many children. While such cases may be pathetic, they must not be considered average, and here it is illness and poverty that are the culprits, together, perhaps, with a poor understanding of the techniques which make rhythm successful.

We will come to grips with her flat statement about its efficacy, and the dreadful havoc it wreaks.

Let us proceed to the average family, attempting to apply the rhythm principles. Mrs. Ruether warns of the terrible danger of "continual calculation . . . interminable worry" tending to "erode their serenity and to create serious repercussions in the whole family."

What follows is a fantastic picture of mindless, bestial behavior: Husbands "explode in helpless rage." Wives "become hysterical." Parents take out their "fear and resentment on their children."

But a little later on, she says, "Actually, self-control is really a minor problem."

The above-pictured individuals seem to us to have quite a

problem of self-control. We wonder what would happen if the man had trouble with his job, or the woman had mother-in-law trouble, or if a really serious problem of illness or financial difficulty arose; but then, of course, we must understand that only the practice of rhythm induces such hyper-mania in otherwise normal human beings.

If, indeed, it is so, that our churches are attended by people of such inclination—and none are known to us—it is surprising that we do not lead the nation with our divorce rate, as well as our birth rate.

But then, after playing the difficulty of self control for all its weight in editor's gold, she says that controlling one's passions isn't really the main objection. The whole trouble is "a matter of destroying some positive good in the marital relationship ... by having to abstain in the middle of the month"—which she incorrectly cites as the time when all women have the greatest sexual inclination—and by losing all that "spontaneity."

Apparently those who use contraceptives never lose any spontaneity, while ours is just oozing away. Somehow we juxtapose this in the mind's eye with a gal murmuring, "Just a moment, darling," while she disappears frantically into the bathroom for a little "protection"—or her husband tests a condom by inflating it to gigantic proportions. Just a little gap in the spontaneity.

She has all this culminating with some women even feeling "an abhorrence of sex ... under such pressure." We did not realize the frigid wife was a Catholic phenomenon. The perversions of contraception are more likely than temporary abstinence to lead to frigidity.

She then appoints the woman as "the policeman of the marital bed." Actually, our own method, as we discussed in the first chapter, makes the husband the Chief of Police, with the wife deputized to make daily progress reports, to be interpreted by both, with mutual intelligence and understanding.

Her attitude is reflecting the extreme attitudes adopted by many people when confronted with some greater or lesser degree of failure in the practice of rhythm.

But she is having it two ways: she is saying, in effect, "I don't believe in it because it doesn't work," and she is saying, "When you do make it work, it's no good for the marriage." Just as she is saying, "It pushes people beyond the bounds of self control," and then, paradoxically, "Self control isn't really the problem, anyway."

By the way, she also admits that there is a not infrequent incidence of failure in the use of contraceptives, and one wonders about the state of mind of those using a method which they must realize may fail them at any time. Following her premise, they must all be hoarse with hysteria and bald with anxiety.

Please do not feel that we see no validity in the mention of difficulties connected with the practice of rhythm. That's what this book is about. But we just had to give that pendulum a big swing in the other direction, after reading that article.

We have quoted and refuted Mrs. Ruether at length, because we feel she displays, in this article and later writings, a sharp picture of the negative thinking which lies at the opposite pole to the positive state of mind which is a prerequisite to the successful practice of rhythm.

Just as she is emphasizing a state of mind, we also wish to emphasize a state of mind which must be embraced by both partners.

Just as one's attitude toward life can make one happy or miserable, one's attitude toward the practice of rhythm is the key to failure or success. Resentment of one's partner because of the practice of rhythm is a certain step to pregnancy.

An offshoot of the "spontaneity" state of mind is the habit some couples have adopted of quarreling and "making up" as the great thing in their love lives. They play it as a harmless little game which culminates in a dramatic reunion.

If they have really mastered this dangerous dance, and know all the steps, they can probably also abstain from indulging in it. If they are using it as a crutch in their relationship, it really has to go, anyway, before one of them makes a false step and the marriage takes a tumble.

*   *   *

Let us assume you have had a most pleasant period of sexual relations, lasting anywhere from two to three weeks. You realize with regret that it is your last night. You perform the act with fervor, not unmixed with a sense of premature nostalgia; and satiated, fall into a deep sleep.

Within eight hours you're ready to go again.

The strange thing about it is that you didn't feel this way yesterday morning, or the morning before that. But the knowledge that the sweet ecstasy on the other side of the bed—your spouse—is, by your own decision, temporarily not available to you, seems to activate unseemly desire.

The first thing to do is get out of bed. We realize this is never easy, under any circumstances, but it is an important factor in the successful practice of rhythm.

You are now out of bed, we hope—after all, aside from not getting pregnant, you do have work to do—and you realize, with firm resolve, that for the next eight to fourteen days you will be celibate.

That isn't nearly as difficult as it sounds. It isn't the true celibacy of a priest or nun. It's only temporary. And just as they receive spiritual and temporal compensations, so will you.

Now, how do we manage to get through this period of time without:

1. Committing sin.
2. Becoming irritable.
3. Going into a catatonic state.

And secondly, how can we derive benefits which are both spiritual and sexual?

The first requirement is daily prayer. The morning offering is particularly suitable; not only in the morning, but at each time during the day that you find yourself quivering with lust.

The common definition of "lust" has a degrading and sinful connotation. This is not necessarily true. We prefer to think of lust—when we think about it at all, which is often —as "sensuous desire, bodily appetite, longing or eagerness to enjoy."

Half the pleasure of abstinence is that this is your chance to enjoy lust.

The amount of difficulty encountered during the time of abstinence will vary from month to month; and, indeed, will vary radically from day to day. Some days are better, some days are worse.

We hope you don't think you have to do this all by yourselves. God is going to help you, if you like. So we say "prayer", but it can be as vague a word as "love." Seek out ways to substantiate this human ideal of creative prayer.

You may find, as we have, that the practice of an aspiration at frequent intervals during those occasional difficult days not only cools the fires, but develops a personal feeling of a small touch of sanctity.

Recently, on the Feast of the Holy Name, it was made a little more clear to us what a tremendous prayer "Jesus" is: when you say it or think it, you have to think of Him.

"My Jesus, all for love of Thee."

It helps, immeasurably.

For many of us the real beginning of the love of God accompanies the onset of parenthood, the miracle of life and our responsibility to it and for it. We know we're really going to need God now that we're parents. We have our first experience with giving in a less selfish way, and we begin to understand God's love a little better. Perhaps we start to love our own parents in a finer, more mature way, because we are no longer just taking love, or trading it.

Up to this point some of us may have felt God's love mainly as being bestowed on us as a child of fortune, and feeling it couldn't happen to a nicer guy, or gal. When we start to understand that we have to cooperate with God's love, we probably want to inquire a little further into the nature of that love.

Perhaps it is trite to recommend inspirational reading, but we will, anyway. You may be astounded at the boom in good Catholic philosophical reading. By "philosophical", we do not mean academically, but practically written.

One drawback to seeking spiritual insight from moral and philosophical reading is that the utter truth and beauty that come from some of our finest writers are most readily recognized and understood by people who have already discovered these truths for themselves.

Again at the risk of sounding trite, have these men who

holler loudest about abstaining ever tried early rising for
daily Mass? Or prayed the rosary on the way to work? Or
spent ten seconds a day contemplating the crucifix in their
bedroom? We have been promised, after all, the graces necessary for our state in life. But we do have some obligation to
cooperate in obtaining them.

It would be interesting to speculate on the mentality of the
man who complains about the impossibility of abstinence as
he turns the pages of *Playboy* magazine.

This is the time of the month when you can accomplish
some of the things you keep telling yourself you want to do,
or ought to do, but don't have the time or energy for when
you wish to preserve your time and energy for making love.

For instance, you can spend some time with the children.
You won't have to sit them in front of the television set on
Sunday afternoon and pretend Mommy and Daddy are going
to take a nap. You can watch the same program they're
watching; or, better yet, play a game with them, or find out
why they're failing in arithmetic.

When you discover that you can't understand how to re-
duce complex fractions to their lowest common denominator,
and change them to percentages, either, passion will be
smothered with panic. Let's not even talk about the "new
math."

If you're a man in a business where your free time can be
devoted to extra work, this is your opportunity to make a
little extra money, so you won't have to spend so much time
at work next week when your wife is spraying the boudoir
with perfume.

You can walk through the house turning out the lights
which your children and wife have left burning in the
empty rooms. This not only uses up energy, it turns one's

thoughts to meeting the electric bill, the gas bill and the mortgage payment.

These thoughts discourage sex.

That tile in the kitchen has to be repaired, too. The stove is in terrible condition. The hem has to be let down on your daughter's uniform. You promised to explain to your son why we have wars. The dog needs a bath. You haven't written to your Aunt Margaret since last Christmas.

(Don't tell us you haven't got an Aunt Margaret. Everybody has an Aunt Margaret.)

And you know perfectly well you're not going to want to bother with any of that stuff in another ten days when you can devote yourself to the pursuit of sexual love.

Do these things now. They will contribute to a state of fatigue, which is another asset in the practice of abstinence. There's nothing better than a good, healthy state of utter physical and emotional exhaustion to extinguish the fires of passion.

This is what makes us wonder about those supposed people who are being made hysterical and demoniac by abstinence. Is there nothing else in their lives which demands the consumption of time, energy and passion? What a waste not to turn that fierce drive in another direction for a while.

If you find that you are becoming physically stirred no matter what you do to divert yourself, stop thinking about yourself, and direct your thoughts and attentions to the spiritual and emotional needs of your mate.

This doesn't mean you have to pretend that sex doesn't exist during this time. Not only is this a grave error, your body keeps telling you it's a dirty lie. Agree with your body. Sex does exist. And compromise.

If you're troubled with impure thoughts, well, think about

your spouse. You'll still be having sexy thoughts, but they won't be impure, and as a married person you have a right to sexual thoughts of your mate.

Abstract thoughts of sex, which later can be localized or focused, are normal in each of us. Learn to use them as a foundation for a better sexual relationship with your husband or wife.

There is absolutely no reason to be afraid to kiss your husband. If you are feeling particularly affectionate, by all means caress your wife. A little friendly bottom-patting will do wonders for the psyche.

We know a couple who never kiss each other when they're abstaining. This puts a certain strain on their marriage, because it makes them look, even to themselves, as if they're mad at each other. This is carrying abstinence too far, and is a result of a basic misunderstanding of what it takes to make rhythm work.

It takes love, love and more love. It won't work without it. And if that love exists, it has to be expressed. Love cannot survive in a vacuum. At every opportunity, you must remind one another of that beautiful, glorious, God-given truth:

"I love you, Darling."

Our hearts and bodies cry for attention and affection. Gratify them. There's no law that says you have to consummate. And you may be surprised to find that a mild petting session satisfies the body in a unique way, by really satisfying the psychological urge for physical contact, mutual understanding and spiritual union.

As with every other part of marriage, of course, this must be done with care, thoughtfulness and respect. Remember the word "mutual." Abstinence is no time for "teasing." You must be always mindful of your partner's limits of endurance, and balance them against the basic requirements of affection.

Teasing is primarily a matter of the ego. We are ego-sensitive creatures, and want to be noticed. If love and affection are displayed during the period of abstinence, there should be no desire to inflame your mate to prove to yourself that you are as desirable as you were on your wedding night.

An honest effort must be made to avoid those situations which you know will give rise to extremely erotic feelings. Paradoxically, however, there may come an occasion when the very use of erotic impulse can be used as an aid to the practice of abstinence.

We cannot recommend to the average reader that you lock the bedroom door during abstinence and indulge in loveplay. However, if you are confident you have a sufficient amount of control to spend half an hour loving without consummating, you will find that you are expressing yourselves in ways you don't take time to bother with when you're "on." This is also a most satisfying experience, in its own unique way.

Just set the alarm for a reasonable period of time. If you think you can "cuddle" for an hour without danger or undue discomfort, set the clock for thirty minutes. (During the daylight hours, preferably).

You'll hate that bell when it rings. But get up, make a pot of coffee, and get back to that letter to Aunt Margaret.

After the first few minutes following this practice of sexual love without sexual intercourse, you will find that it has satisfied sexual desire for a time.

We don't recommend this as a frequent or constant practice during the time of abstinence. Once a month, at the most. A good time is about midway along. (This is also the time of the most fertile period of the wife, so don't get carried away).

If you can get through the month without trying this, by all means do so. And don't try it when you have only a few more days to wait. This tends to develop an attitude of, "We're probably safe."

Forget it. You're probably not.

This seems to be a good place to quash the rumor—or misconception, if we may—that a woman feels the most passion at the time of ovulation, and therefore abstinence at that time causes an undue and intolerable hardship. The fact of the matter is that most women feel no more passion at that time of the month than at any other time. The passion she experiences is the result of the several days' abstinence preceding ovulation. If you don't believe us, try abstaining during the "safe" period, and see if it's any easier.

As a matter of fact, your male author has noticed that *he* feels more passion at the time of ovulation.

Another method of sublimation for the husband is to buy some sexy nightwear for his wife. The heady excitement of striding purposefully up to a lingerie counter and buying a filmy little nothing, without hesitation as to the right size— *that's* savoir faire—and giving his wife this intimate gift, will again placate the psychological desire to express to her his passion and his love.

For those so inclined, the use of humorously sexy remarks (tete-a-tete) may prove to be an outlet for sex impulse. The development of these verbal intimacies to a high degree of finesse, polish and subtlety is a consummation devoutly to be wished.

It's like getting a card in the mail from an old friend, saying simply and sincerely, "Thinking of you."

If, in spite of everything, you find a growing irritability in your outlook toward life, directly attributable to a gnawing in your loins, take turns. Don't both display irritability at the same time.

This develops a strong sense of fair play in a marriage. After all, it is his turn. You were in a foul mood yesterday, although maybe the children all coming down with measles had something to do with it.

If mutual respect is maintained between a wife and husband, antagonisms should not develop. The woman should understand that in most cases the practice of rhythm involves a greater sacrifice on the part of the man. His desire is more frequent, and more physically obvious. He is more prone to sexual thoughts, and a lively reaction to them.

If any woman wants to dispute this, let us inquire how many of you are ready for sex immediately upon awakening?

As a general rule—and we admit there are some exceptions —it is the woman who desires most strongly to limit the size of her family, or to space the births.

Realize, then, that he is doing this for love of you. Appreciate his sacrifice. Give him the credit he deserves. And fill his other physical and emotional needs with love, understanding and generous effort.

The man, on the other hand, should not dramatize himself as a martyr. He should not blame his wife in any way for his temporary discomfort. The devotion and appreciation which he will receive from his wife, in return for his consideration of her, will more than compensate him for any sexual deprivation.

He should remember that this woman is the same delightful creature who shares his bed and his passion in that most intimate of physical and spiritual relationships at other times during the month. The fact that physical intimacy has been temporarily discontinued does not mean that love has failed, that desire has expired, or that this woman is not thoroughly and completely entitled to every drop of love, tenderness and blood in a man's heart.

He is not in the least being heroic by practicing rhythm; but he can practice rhythm heroically.

The expression of sexual love in marriage is demonstrated by much more than the act of sexual intercourse. Those little manifestations of love between a man and woman, the small things that embellish a marriage, as flowers embellish an altar, should become more evident.

Marriage requires repeated courtship. Use your period of abstinence wisely. This is the best time to have a "date" with your mate. Don't plan on going out to dinner and a show when you can be doing much better things. Such as making love.

Be grateful for abstinence. Its contribution to a strong Christian marriage is a significant factor in building that marriage to withstand the heavier crosses that God may send.

And within a day or two of the start of your next honeymoon—because that's what it is, another honeymoon every month—you will find that sex is becoming increasingly vital.

Not unlike your wedding day, you'll find yourself thinking about it more and more as the time draws closer. You'll read your charts, and make your plans, and tremble in anticipation of the renewal of that ever-old, but again new, first passionate embrace.

You will, in short, never become careless about sexual love.

CHAPTER 4

CREATIVE SEX

A marriage is not truly born until the honeymoon is over. It is only when facing the sometimes ugly, sometimes beautiful realities of existence that two people can become one.

The honeymoon is an escape from the world. Marriage can be a conquest of, a compromise with, or a surrender to the world.

It cannot be an escape.

During the authors' short and ecstatic honeymoon, there was one hour, and one hour only, when the world literally did not exist. There was wet sand beneath our bare feet, and clear water lapping at our toes, and we walked alone on an empty beach under a hazy morning sky, and water and sky met and melted without horizon, and were one, as were we.

Sound and speech were unknown. Our touching fingers were our only reality, and held our souls together in this wondrous place. We existed on a plane that did not exist.

It lasted for an hour, and then it was gone. It will never return, nor will its passing be mourned. It was a doorway through which we had to pass to find something better. Hand in hand, we passed through that doorway, and found ourselves in the world of creative sex.

No, no, not *pro*creative. *Creative*.

Sex is more than a physical and emotional yearning. Sex is more than anticipation, momentary pleasure and a good night's sleep.

Sex is the glue that binds a marriage together.

Sexual attraction precedes love. Sexual fulfillment accompanies the growth of love. Sexual fulfillment is more than an orgasm. It encompasses our entire being. It is a woman's feminity, a man's masculinity.

Our sex expresses itself in the way we walk and talk, and laugh and cry. It makes itself known in the way we look at life, our desire for security, our yearning for adventure.

Without God, we are nothing. Without sex, we are less than what we are. For we are sexual creatures. Each of us has a sexual image of self. As the body and soul are one, so too with sex and ego, sexual image and self. We cannot have a satisfactory sexual relationship in marriage unless we have a strong sexual awareness of self, and a high sexual opinion of our mate.

It would be difficult to expect too much from sex. Sex is a gift from God, and like all of His gifts, when properly used, it grants to its receiver, here on earth, almost heavenly joys. But we very often expect the wrong things from a sexual relationship because of the distorted and unreal view of sex that permeates our society.

Sex in marriage can suffer because of this.

Our lives are beset with insidious sex symbols. "This girl," they cry, "is America's sex symbol." "This man," they proclaim, "is virility personified." "His back is strong and straight," they moan. "Her figure is glorious. How can you settle for less?"

They are fools, and only fools will listen.

Your mate is your sex symbol.

Beautiful or homely, bald or curly-headed, flat or curved, weak or strong, you are the sex symbol for your mate.

This is the gift God has given you. Only in this way can sex be used to grant its limitless joys, its endless gratifications, its almost unbearable ecstasies. And only in this way will it make the marriage grow, in love and with love, to His ultimate love.

It has been said that marriage is a method by which two people decide to achieve salvation together, instead of separately. A good sexual foundation will strengthen a good marriage, and a good marriage is one of the easiest paths to salvation.

Quite basically, the success of rhythm depends on the success of the marriage. An unhappy marriage will not produce happy results in rhythm. The factors which result in a satisfying marriage are the same factors necessary for the satisfactory practice of rhythm.

It seems here we should differentiate between the words "perfect" and "satisfactory." Each one of us, surfboarding along on the waves of courtship, has looked forward to a "perfect" marriage.

After the honeymoon, sooner or later, the first imperfections appear—we are, after all, God's imperfect creatures—and those couples who take these imperfections as objects of love and affection, rather than defects in their love, are those who truly arrive, paradoxically, at a "perfect" marriage.

The same distinction must be made between the "perfect" practice of rhythm and the "satisfactory" practice of rhythm.

Again, since we are imperfect creatures, the possibility of error must always be considered. And it is for this reason that we say that engaged couples and young married men and women, as much as older married people—if not more so—should begin their study of the rhythm method of birth control before they have occasion to require it.

If it is true that the primary purpose of marriage is the procreation and education of children, it must be admitted that this does not require the newlywed couple to conceive a child during their first month, or first three months, or even their first year of marriage.

What better time to study the intricacies of the rhythm method? What finer occasion will ever exist for two people, man and wife, to educate themselves in the control of their passions, and to acquire the knowledge and ability that will enable them, in later years, to limit their families without any possibility of the moral earthquakes that shake those with large families, and no place to go but to contraception?

This is the time to learn, and this is the time to experiment. And when experimentation with "cutting down" the period of abstinence results in a pregnancy, it will serve a two-fold purpose: that of adding additional information to the practice of rhythm—("Boy, we sure can't cut it down that far, can we?")—and at the same time giving the couple that which they have a responsibility to produce, the fruit of their love, the blossom of new life, the child which will make them a family.

We who practice rhythm have a great advantage over those who do not in the sex education of our children. To our young men and women we can say:

"Marriage is not license. It requires the highest degree of self-control and restraint. Marriage is not a constant fulfillment of sexual desire; it is a continual fulfillment, with sex, of selfless love."

Marriage, contrary to the popular statement, is not a fifty-fifty proposition. It is something closer to hundred-hundred. This allows for errors, and even the best marriages will have errors, and must be flanked on both sides with generous broad margins to compensate for them.

To cite one of the many objections to this numerical approach: since each of us is most tolerant of his (her) own shortcomings—maybe even blind to them—to aim for fifty per cent might well be to hit thirty.

Perhaps each spouse should do a little psychological stage directing, and say to himself—or herself—"I really should assume one hundred per cent of the burden, since undoubtedly I am the morally stronger."

If any among you does not think he (she) is the morally stronger, you must have an inferiority complex.

You are no longer responsible for only the salvation of your own soul. The obligation of leading your mate to the arms of God now rests heavily on your shoulders, and if each of you accepts that responsibility as entirely yours, each of you will find the path—together—easy, sure, and dappled with sunlight.

Marriage, although sometimes involved with addition and multiplication, is not a mathematical science. It is not, contrary to some modern psychological thinking—or the hopes of the cyberneticists, eager to mate us according to an IBM machine —even an inexact science.

At its best, marriage is an art, and the artful spouse will dip into the soul's own palette to bring to the canvas of marriage the color and composition that will make that marriage a masterpiece.

It is difficult to imagine a couple developing a "perfect" marriage and surmounting all the obstacles, objective and subjective, that come our way, without that marriage being imbued with a strong spirituality. It might come first, or as a result of the struggle towards perfection, but it would ultimately have to exist in a "perfect" marriage.

Sex becomes more meaningful when it reflects a close relationship in all other areas of the marriage. Both marriage and rhythm depend on cooperation and consideration. The outward signs of love may appear perfunctory. They are not. They are a reaffirmation of love.

The development of one's own faculty of loving, independent of the object of love, is the surest method of insuring the growth of that love which is your marriage.

In the development of the faculty of loving, we cannot say too much for the practical application of your religious beliefs. In the case of the Christian, this certainly includes love demonstrated through charity, sacrifice and self-discipline. Indeed, these three read like a definition of "tenderness," a very basic ingredient in any loving relationship.

It is important that a man think not of his masculinity in terms of uncontrolled virility. If there is any one virtue that makes rhythm work, that virtue is charity. For if a man loves his wife as God loves His church, he will visit upon her only those burdens which she is physically and psychologically able to accept.

Virility, the "white plume" which each man wears proudly and unstained, encompasses more than the ability to obtain an erection. If a man is a man, in the fullest meaning of the word, and thereby lays claim to virility, it is presupposed that he also has the strength of character and will to subdue his desire.

Is the mark of a man the frequency with which he enjoys sexual relations? We do not believe so. The truly virile man needs no reminder that his wife's body is a temple, not merely a vessel for his pleasure, a repository for his body.

We are not saying that "too much sex" between a husband and wife is evil. Nor are we denying the reasonable right of each partner to the other's body.

We are saying that hedonism—the love of pleasure for its own sake—is a heinous and destructive way of life, and that the rights and privileges of married life must be counterbalanced with an acceptance of the obligations which marriage brings, which obligations include, but are not limited to, the sanctification of one another, and the procreation and education of children.

It is probable that by this time you are aware of the authors' views of the roles we play in married life, and our attitudes toward marriage. We do not pretend that they are perfect, but we feel they are taking us in the right direction.

We have become aware that there are a certain number of men who pose quite a problem to their wives by reason of their attitude. Even allowing for greater passion in the average male, this does not quite explain their resistance to a moderate curtailing of their sexual activity.

There are a number of wives who wistfully interpret this attitude as indifference to the best interests of wife and family. We hear again and again, "Surely, love and concern for me and the children should make the cross of a moderate period of abstinence bearable."

Our own opinion is that it is seldom lack of love—lack of perfect love, yes—nor is it strictly a physical compulsion.

Very often the culprit is misinterpretation by the man of his role. This misinterpretation is often induced by the strong tendency in our society to equate masculinity with animal passion.

The paradoxical outcome of many situations where the male is reluctant to subject his passion to any moderate restraint is that finally, when the situation becomes desperate, we find many of these couples resorting hysterically to unreasonably long periods of abstinence, disoriented from any logical method.

We have heard of examples such as six months complete and total abstinence, and then conception occurring upon their first coitus following this epical demonstration. This is clearly a matter of the male being confused about his role.

You got married to do things together, all sorts of good things. True, different types of people prefer different degrees of togetherness; but whatever degree it may be, it has to be fulfilled, with charity.

You have to strike the right balance between comfortable familiarity, striving for growth, and the development of variety and refinements in your love. The art of making love certainly involves a great deal more than the ability to consummate, or the frequency with which the act is performed.

Indeed, how can one "make love," in the fullest sense of the phrase, and not begin with charity? For love is a giving, not a taking, and it is the giving of oneself in the physical act of love which makes the pleasure from that act increase with every passing year of married life, and makes one, at long last, a consummate lover.

Wives, treat your husbands as if you were trying to make all other men envious of him.

Men, treat your wives as if you were still courting them. After all, a woman's sexual responses are based more on emotion than on physical desire. She will not be as responsive sexually if the man does not respond in other areas of life. Bolster your mate's sexual ego; and by this we mean in every facet of your mate's character and personality. You cannot belittle one another in the living room and expect to later achieve happiness in the bedroom.

Share the burdens of marriage. Even in a good marriage, the burdens are heavy, and while the joyful acceptance of one's own responsibilities is the surest path to happiness, if one feels overburdened with responsibility and duty it is likely the normal human reaction will be resentment, rather than joy.

Don't relegate sex to the last thing at night. Sex is more important than an afterthought, the tail end of one's time and energy.

Have a love affair with your mate. It's easy, inexpensive and rewarding. Raise the quality to compensate for quantity; and, ingenious paradox, if your period of lovemaking is satisfying and exciting, your period of abstinence will be that much less difficult.

Wives, it is altogether prudent to "neglect" your children to keep your husband inspired. The housework can wait. Your man is more interested in a lovely, loving you to bolster his ego, after his daily battle with the world, than he is in a vacuumed floor.

He wants to feel that he is a man, just as you want to feel that you are a woman.

Your mate comes first: before money, before the household chores, before the children. You can give no greater gift to your child than the strong bond of love between their father and mother.

This is what a marriage is supposed to be, love between a man and a woman. Not an overwhelming pre-occupation with position, family or house. Your spouse is your first love, your first duty, and your first line of defense, and it is on this unshakeable foundation that you are able to give to your children the "allness" of you to which they are entitled.

The more you give to your mate, the more you will have to give to your children, who are the primary purpose of your marriage. If it were not for their children, your authors would leave behind the dubious benefits of civilization, and spend their remaining days 'neath the waving palms, playing footsie on the warm sands of a sun-drenched isle in the Blue Pacific.

We still plan on it, as a matter of fact, but the Blue Pacific is in the mind of the beholder, and the palm trees grow where you plant them in your life.

The cliché of this attitude is the candlelit dinner for two. This is fine, if you can find time for it. More to the point, perhaps, is a backrub for that tired husband of yours, even though your hands do ache. And one of the deepest expressions of love that a man can demonstrate is to get out of bed on a cold night—during the time of abstinence, of course—to fix his wife's hot water bottle.

(For some reason that your male author finds inexplicable, women seem to have a "thing" about a hot water bottle. This author does not know whether it is physical or psychological, but he certainly does not know any men who confess to sleeping with a hot water bottle. Certainly none of his friends in the Army ever did.)

(He admits it is perhaps possible that men are missing a good deal, but the whole concept seems quite effeminate, probably because women have so wholeheartedly embraced it for themselves.)

(This is from your other author. I don't know why, either,

but it just relaxes me. Maybe it's an outward sign of the female yearning for security.)

Feed your sense of humor. If you let the grimness of the frustrations of your daily life over-shadow mirth, you are killing love. Life is difficult without a sense of humor. Love is impossible. The "life is real, life is earnest" approach would make child-rearing an intolerable hardship. When one has four daughters, as we have, two of them beginning their Great Struggle with Adolescence, we find at times that a well-developed sense of the ridiculous is our hope, our refuge and our strength. Sometimes we even get hysterical.

Keep alive your enthusiasms, share them with your family, and let them share theirs with you. The marital and parental adjustments that must be made between man and woman, parent and child in a good Christian family are impossible without using God's gift of enthusiasm. And, oh, how an enthusiasm for Love can overwhelm and encompass the physical desire for "making love."

And perhaps most important of all, maintain and develop your lines of communication. The writing of this book is a case in point. Each of your authors has a full-time job— father and bread-winner, mother and home manager. Tremendous adjustments in family life became necessary to find time to research and write, and these adjustments required more generosity than was necessary in the practice of rhythm.

As rhythm begets love in marriage, by the use of creative sex, so each of us brought to this book the fullness of self, the richness of sexuality and a marriage of our deepest beliefs. It was more than a literary work. It was a sexually creative act.

Talk to one another. Not only at the dinner table, but in bed. Not only about the problems of the day, but your plans for the future. Build your palaces, and let their spires punch holes in the sky. It doesn't really matter if they ever come to pass. The important thing is that you made them together, and believed in them, together.

It is not enough to sleep together.

You must also dream together.

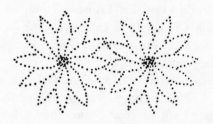

CHAPTER 5

THE EGG AND YOU, THE SPERM AND I

We had finished dinner, and were lingering over our coffee. Our guests were a Catholic couple, enjoying a high-income bracket, and possessing college educations and three children.

The discussion had at last come, as it will—under our astute and sneaky direction—to birth control.

"I think the Church is wrong," said our male guest, (a practicing Catholic,) "but the great theologians say I'm wrong. We practice rhythm, but we don't think we should have to."

Thus we began with the morality or immorality of contraception, and arrived ultimately at the physiology and practice of rhythm.

"At the time of ovulation," I began—

"Ovulation?" asked my college-educated friend. "What's that?"

Astonishment was hardly the word for our reaction. Here were people who we had assumed were intelligent, educated

59

and aware of the basic vocabulary one expects to find in today's American, and certainly in a married person.

We must admit that after about three seconds, he finally recovered himself and said, "Oh, you mean when the egg comes out." Yes, that's what we meant, and the word is "ovulation."

It is amusing to contemplate the significance of this same person presuming to disagree with the "great theologians" on the matters of moral law.

This was not the first time we had been confronted with the surprising lack of knowledge that a great many Catholics have, not only about rhythm—ignoring for the moment their appalling ignorance in theology—but about the basic biological vocabulary and the physiological facts to which that vocabulary refers.

On one occasion, a Catholic friend with eight children referred to the monthly bleeding period of his wife as something that can only be translated as "administration."

He and his wife were having difficulty with the successful practice of rhythm. They had begun their attempts to practice family limitation after the birth of their fifth child. He was, at this point, seriously considering methods condemned by the Church.

We would like to point out that it would be hard, to our mind, to achieve success in rhythm, or any other endeavor, without having knowledge of the vocabulary of the particular subject.

On another occasion, two girl friends—of the female author, not the male—boy, wouldn't that be something!—were visiting for a few days. They were Catholic, and both had rather large families. We wondered whether the question of birth control would arise.

It did, within five minutes after they got off the train, and continued until they left.

One of them was in the early stages of pregnancy. The other, we determined, was in her "safe" period.

They were attempting, they thought, to practice rhythm. Neither of them had ever read a book on the subject. They were making up their own rules as they went along. One of them told us that she and her husband had abstained for forty-seven days, and she still got pregnant. Each was convinced that her trouble must be that she ovulated twice every month.

Their husbands joined them later in the week. From the sounds of merriment emanating from their sleeping quarters, it was obvious to our sensitive ears that they were enjoying conjugal love.

Unfortunately, it was the wrong time of the month for us. It was a terrible night.

But bearing no hard feelings, we subsequently advised them as fully as we could on the subject of rhythm, and gave them some books to read.

Substantially, this is what we told them:

This is an egg:

This is a sperm:

This is imminent conception:

About once each month—or to be more accurate, once each menstrual cycle—the woman releases, from her ovaries, one or more eggs. One egg is the usual procedure, unless we wish to consider the possibility of twins, triplets, and so on, which we'd rather not think about.

The egg, or ovum, is released between twelve and sixteen days *before* the start of the next menstrual (bleeding) period. It is thought that most usually it is the fourteenth or fifteenth day before menstruation; but the outside, liberal range is twelve to sixteen days.

Sperms, on the other hand, are released by the millions in the seminal fluid ejaculated by the male during intercourse.

Imagine the scene: millions and millions of wriggling sperms searching frantically for an egg to fertilize. If the egg is anywhere around, one healthy sperm, out of those millions, will undoubtedly find it, penetrate it and fertilize it.

However, even a healthy sperm doesn't live very long.

Neither does an egg.

Dr. M. Edward Davis, in his book, *"Natural Child Spacing,"** says:

> "The life of the unfertilized egg is extremely short, probably less than twenty-four hours."

In *"The Modern Method of Birth Control,"*[1] Dr. Thurston S. Welton states:

> "The ovum cannot be fertilized after it is twenty-four hours old."

Dr. John Marshall, in *"The Infertile Period,"*[2] had this to say:

> "At the outside, therefore, the ovum may be fertilized for up to forty-eight hours after ovulation, though the bulk of the evidence suggests that the period is very much less than this, probably in the region of twelve to twenty-four hours."

Again, Dr. Davis:

> "The sperm cells ... survive for twenty-four or thirty-six hours."

Dr. Welton:[3] "It is therefore concluded that the father-cells

---

* Hanover House, 1953, p. 42.
1 Grosset and Dunlap, 1954, p. 24.
2 Helicon Press, 1963, p. 12.
3 l.c., p. 25.

have a limited lifespan. The limit is placed at forty-eight hours."

A somewhat more liberal view is taken by Dr. J. G. H. Holt, in *"Marriage and Periodic Abstinence"*:[4]

"We may reasonably assume that the fertilizing capacity of human spermatozoa is not more than forty-eight hours. We, in practice, reckon seventy-two hours, and from our many cases it has been proved that this term is cautious and even ample."

And finally, Dr. Marshall:[5]

"The evidence, therefore, suggests that the sperms do not survive for more than three days after intercourse in the average case, though the possibility of longer survival in exceptional cases must be recognized."

We should mention here that some objectors to the rhythm method have recently claimed that the sperm may live as long as one week in the vaginal tract. Their argument is fallacious, and even such a pro-contraceptive scientist as Leon F. Whitney, in his book *"Birth Control Today,"*[6] says:

"They do live longer than that, but they do not fertilize unless they are very fresh. (Forty-eight hours at most)."

Taking the conservative estimates of life expectancy of the egg and the sperm—24 hours and 48 hours, respectively—we have a maximum figure of 72 hours a cycle during which conception can occur.

That's three days, and three days only.

Unless you are convinced, as most men are, that you are more virile than the average man, in which case your sperm might live 72 hours, thereby creating a four-day possibility of conception.

---

4 Longmans, 1961, p. 40.
5 l.c., p. 12.
6 Collier Books, 1960, p. 70.

Or, if you are a terribly fertile woman—and which of you would deny that you are—your egg might live forty-eight hours. Therefore, we have a liberal grand total of five days out of each cycle during which pregnancy could or might occur.

If the egg is not fertilized within its short lifespan, it will die and be discharged twelve to sixteen days later with the menstrual fluid.

If the egg is not present, within forty-eight (or seventy-two) hours the sperm will die.

If the egg is present, and is fertilized, you are pregnant. Both of you.

It is the opinion of one of the authors that men suffer during pregnancy at least as much as women do, if not more.

It is the opinion of the other author that while the husband may suffer reflected discomfort, he just doesn't *know* what a woman goes through.

This is the only point on which your authors will disagree, so don't stand around waiting for a fight.

As to the oft-blamed "whipping boy," double ovulation, not only are such cases extremely rare, but where they do occur, the two ovulations must occur at about the same time, usually within twenty-four hours.

Dr. Marshall has this to say about double ovulation:[7]

"All the evidence favours the view that because of hormonal control both ovulations occur about the same time ... The secretion of the corpus luteum formed after the first ovulation suppresses the ripening of more follicles."

We have found that a surprising number of people attempting to practice rhythm:

---

7 l.c., pp. 53-54.

1. Don't understand the vocabulary;
2. Haven't read any book whatsoever on the subject, and are attempting to practice rhythm by a hit-and-miss method of counting days *after* menstruation. Including those who have discussed it with their doctor, and come away filled with misinformation.

(Let's not even *think* about the woman who is practicing rhythm on the basis of back-fence gossip, and has the whole thing backwards).

3. Have read a book on the subject, but have been unable to apply the scientific information contained therein to their own particular and individual cases, because of the ambiguities, conflicting statements and generally over-simplified (or utterly confusing) examples that are given in some texts.

We hope that our book will encourage and assist these people to understand rhythm, and to learn to apply these facts in a practical way.

It is our experience, based on personal knowledge and countless discussions with others, that unwanted pregnancies which occur during the practice of rhythm are caused by:

1. Impatience.
2. Lack of knowledge.
3. Misinterpretation of the charts.

The laws of nature must be obeyed. They should, most certainly, be understood. And the charts must be read correctly.

They can be, as you will see.

CHAPTER 6

THE UPS AND DOWNS OF RHYTHM

"Rhythm" refers to the use of the marital right during the two sterile portions of the cycle, and refraining from sexual intercourse during the time of fertility.

Now, the big question: When is the fertile time? We have experimented with three methods for fixing the time:

1. There is the simple matter of calendar counting, based on the known fact that ovulation occurs twelve to sixteen days before the onset of menstruation, adding two or three days before ovulation for life of the sperm, and one, or two days for life of the ovum after ovulation has occurred.

Thus, in a 28-day cycle, the fertile period during which abstinence would be practiced would be from the 10th through the 17th days of the cycle, inclusive.

A woman using this method would have to calculate for her shortest cycle and her longest cycle—say, 27 to 29—and would therefore abstain from the 9th day through the 18th day, inclusive, every month.

The glaring flaw in this system is that it is based completely upon what your periods have been in the past, not what may occur in the future. Imagine a 31 or 32 day cycle thrown into this picture!

Like the father of seven children who used the calendar method, and told us: "We haven't had a pregacy in two years. We've been lucky."

Well, maybe they'll continue to be lucky. But luck is a thin thread on which to hang one's hopes.

Many women believe they have an absolutely regular 28-day cycle. Such cases, however, are extremely rare. Dr. Holt states that the interval between two menstruations varies in every woman to a certain degree, and that it is quite normal for a woman to have cycles as short as 24 and as long as 35 days or more.

2. The method we have found to be the most revealing as to when ovulation occurs is the body temperature method, which requires taking the temperature daily with a special basal thermometer, available at most drugstores, and recording the daily readings on a chart. This chapter will deal with those charts.

3. The third method is the determination of ovulation by the presence of glucose in the cervical mucus, just prior to, during and just after ovulation, as manifested by sensitized paper changing color on contact. This method will be discussed in the next chapter, along with some comments on the new oral tests which are being developed.

* * *

There are supplementary signs concurrent with, or just prior to ovulation, which may or may not be present in any given individual. Some of these are: pain or pressure on genital organs and/or rectum; sensitivity in the breasts; mucous discharge from the cervix, and particular elasticity of the mucus—called Spinnbarkeit—about the time of ovulation. There may be others. Each woman can attempt to seek out her own "sign", if such be present.

We would use these indications as confirmation of our interpretation of the temperature chart, upon which we place our main reliance.

Women shouldn't be too sure they don't have some or any of the ovulatory signs. Until the time of ovulation was established on our early charts, and we learned that a pain was commonly concurrent with or preceding ovulation, we simply didn't recognize the little rascal.

In fact, at one time your female author went through a series of odious tests as a result of that unrecognized pain, culminating in the swallowing of a large dose of barium, because the doctor wanted to check the condition of her appendix.

The appendix was in fine condition, but the pain was left a mystery for many years. The doctor didn't say, "Oh, well, then it must be *mittelschmerz.*" That's what some German doctor named it. To the American ear it has an important ring, but to the German it's just plain "pain in the middle."

*   *   *

Remember that attitude is a very important factor in the successful practice of rhythm. If you approach it with resentment, or as a whim, without firm reason and purpose, you are bound not to be successful.

We know from our Protestant friends' accounts that a doubtful, lackadaisical approach promotes failure, also, in their use of contraceptives. Not even the best theory can survive the chaos wrought by a reluctant application.

*   *   *

You are awake, and perhaps pulsating with passion. Reach for your basal thermometer and take your temperature. We recommend that you take it rectally. Orally may seem "nicer", but it frequently results in peaks and valleys that bear no relation to ovulation. An accurate temperature may also be taken vaginally.

Mark down the reading before one of your dear children hurls himself into the room and breaks your thermometer. This can happen, and has.

This procedure should begin within a week following the first day of menstruation.

For about the first week or ten days, depending on the length of your cycle, the temperature will remain in the lower level. It will then begin to rise, and within a matter of three to seven days will remain in the upper level.

During this transition from low to high, ovulation has occurred.

Dr. Davis:[1] "The transition from the low level of temperature to the high level is the period of fertility."

Sometimes this rise will be almost meteoric. At other times it will resemble Jack and Jill trying to climb the hill with three broken legs.

One of the supposed objections to the use of the temperature chart is that a woman has too many possible distractions during the night and early morning: getting up with the baby several times at night, some feel, is likely to affect the

---

1 l.c., p. 56.

reading; or the start of mother's day is liable to be hectic
and abrupt, and her "basal" may be all disrupted by the time
she thinks about temperature.

We have found that getting up at night makes little difference, as long as there has been a few hours' rest before
taking the temperature.

Dr. Marshall:[2] "If the mother has been disturbed by the
children during the night a period of an hour in bed before
recording usually gives satisfactory results."

If for any reason it is impossible for you to take your
temperature in the morning, find another time of day, and
adhere to it. Bedtime would be a good second choice.

As for an emergency situation resulting in failure to take
the temperature, you will see some examples of this in our
own charts. It doesn't necessarily matter if you miss a day.
The pattern still exists, and it is this pattern you must learn
to recognize. The more accurate your charts, of course, the
better.

Since illness or physical trauma can affect a cycle, the failure of the chart to follow the expected pattern will warn of
this disrupted cycle, and still show ovulation, even when it
is delayed. (See Chart No. 7.)

Once you have become familiar with your pattern, even an
illness with accompanying fever will not destroy the reada-
bility of your chart, and the use of supplemental tests which
we discuss later can be of great assistance in clarifying and
interpreting those difficult readings.

A typical aberration which can be discounted by an ex-
perienced chart reader would be one high temperature point
disrupting the first, or low plateau, prior to ovulation. After
becoming familiar with your pattern, if you can see that

---

2 l.c., p. 43.

your pattern is being established in the rest of your chart, you may decide to discount the "transient" high point.

We are still unable, at the beginning of the cycle, to determine its length. Although research is being conducted in this field, there is as yet no method to forecast ovulation this far in advance. Therefore, at the beginning of your cycle, you must rely on your judgment and experience in determining your shortest possible period. It is just after the midpoint of your cycle that you will be able to pinpoint its length.

Suppose, for the purpose of demonstration, that you are certain that a 27-day cycle is the shortest possibility. Count the first day of the menstrual period as Cycle Day 1, and the last day of that full cycle, preceding menstruation, as Cycle Day 27. In order to find the day of the cycle which begins the period of abstinence, subtract 18 from the length of the full cycle. 27 less 18 gives us Cycle Day 9, the first day of abstinence for safety with a 27-day cycle. Or, if adding is easier for you, realize that if you start to abstain from relations on Cycle Day 9, you will be safe (add 18) for a 27-day cycle.

The thing to remember is that if you have a cycle longer than any you have ever had, you will be able to see it develop on the chart, and will be warned against resuming relations. However, your only protection against the shorter period is simply to abstain early enough to allow for it. This does not refer to a shorter period in which ovulation takes place at the usual time, but the following menstruation is induced earlier by injury or illness. (See Chart No. 6) Here you have nothing to worry about.

If you do not have sufficient records to estimate your shortest period, the safest thing to do would be to cease relations at the cessation of the menstrual flow, and not resume until the "second safe period" indicated after ovulation. You would continue this over a number of months until you felt your information was sufficient.

Another method, if you feel fairly sure, but are not positive, about your shortest period length, would be to simply shorten it further by a day or so, for good measure. We have kept records for years, and we believe we detect a general shortening in the cycle. Because of this, we have begun to allow for a one-day shorter cycle than in the past. It does become necessary, at times, to re-evaluate your cycle.

As to the last part of the time of abstinence, as you are examining your records you may wish to compute the longest period for which you would be safe at any given time. This is a good double check, especially for beginners. Remember that the number of the cycle day, plus ten, is the period length for which you are absolutely safe. Again, count the first day of menstruation as Cycle Day 1. Therefore, Cycle Day 17, plus ten, is absolutely safe for a 27-day period.

* * *

In *"Marriage and Periodic Abstinence,"*[3] Dr. Holt has introduced an interesting approach to the accurate reading of the basal temperature chart. This book has only recently come to our attention, and we are tremendously enthusiastic about the possibilities inherent in applying his idea.

Dr. Holt has, in effect, established a ratio of temperature rise from low level to high level, as the result of his "studying hundreds of temperature curves for more than twenty years." He demonstrates this by employing boxed-in areas in

---

3 l.c., p. 68.

a related sequence. We have applied this to some of our old charts, retrospectively, and find it most usually reduces the period of abstinence. There are a very few charts to which it cannot be applied because of transient highs or lows.

Dr. Holt believes that when six successive temperature points show in the lower box, and three successive temperature points show in the upper box, sexual relations may be safely resumed.

As you will see from some of the following charts, the day which Dr. Holt prescribes as safe sometimes falls within the "danger" area of twelve to sixteen days before menstruation.

This twelve to sixteen days before menstruation has been authoritatively established as the outside boundaries of the possible range of ovulation in any and every period, although ovulation is most usually believed to occur on the fourteenth or fifteenth day before menstruation.

Since ovulation and the life of the egg consume only a twenty-four hour period, it is apparent that four of the five days within this range are not the day of ovulation. The days preceding ovulation, however, may be fertile, because of the lifespan of the sperm.

If we suppose that ovulation should happen to occur on the fifteenth day before menstruation, the ovum will possibly live through the fourteenth day before menstruation, and the thirteenth and twelfth days before menstruation, in such a cycle, would be safe.

Perhaps Dr. Holt, through his method, is signaling us of the occasions when this occurs. That is why we say that when his method infringes upon the latter limit of the ovulation range—the twelfth and thirteenth days before menstruation—it may well be, nonetheless, quite safe.

We proceed with caution in relying on this without further

data. We think in later charts, with the use of the fertility
tape, we have confirmed his theory.

*   *   *

While our charts will certainly furnish a valuable guide,
they are not at all average in span of continence, since our
records show a possibility of a twenty-six to thirty-six day
menstrual cycle. This verges on what many lay people consider abnormal, and further confirms our belief that the
rhythm method is applicable to highly irregular cycles.

Now, as to keeping records. We have gradually perfected
our record keeping system, but it is to be recommended that
you keep perfect records from the start.

We have always been diligent about writing down the
temperature, which is indeed imperative. And, of course, we
would draw up a detailed graph containing all the important
data, which is also admirable. One then has a tendency to
think of it as done, and rest on one's diligence.

However, since you are going to need these charts to refer
to—a vital procedure in achieving success—it becomes apparent that there is the little matter of adequate filing, too.

Listen to the voice of experience. Don't lose those lovely
detailed records.

We arrived at the excellent solution of keeping our charts
in a looseleaf notebook. This really is ideal, nice and portable,
easily available for quick appraisal. We still do this, and
consider it a great idea, in spite of our terrible setback, which
was the result of one of those little quirks of fate by which
we humans are preyed upon.

It occurred during our last pregnancy. Your female author

takes full blame, because it was due to one of her penny-pinching economy moods that this particular ill-fated notebook was employed.

Our older daughters had brand-new, start of school notebooks, which it turned out were not standard in the class—something to do with number of holes in the paper—and the notebooks were lying among the usual array of apparently abandoned items in their room. One of these, a pretty light blue, was appropriated.

All our records were placed in this, and all went well, until it was left lying out on the bed one day. Our children do not take things from our room, or generally have access to it, but apparently the rightful owner's eye fell upon her property, and she decided to reclaim it.

When its absence was discovered, the culprit produced said notebook, all filled with pristine white pages. To our frantic inquiries as to its previous contents, she summoned up total loss of recall.

At this point we were sure that some of our Protestant neighbors were being treated to an intriguing review of our undercover activities; or, horrors, were under the impression that we were some kind of nuts, passing out our charts to the neighborhood children.

If this sad story can have a happy ending, it was in our finally determining that the old charts had been stuffed into the burning bag, and had gone their way. If you can call that a happy ending.

Is this what people mean when they talk about the difficulties of rhythm?

Oh, by the way, if you have a good friend with whom you think you might compare charts over coffee some morning, *please* be sure you don't get the charts mixed up. That could be disastrous. Be absolutely certain, when you part company, that you have your charts, and she has hers.

*　　*　　*

At this time, let's mention a few of the tools for charting basal ballistics. We still believe in the looseleaf notebook. You need graph paper, lots of it, and don't run out of it. The ideal graph is printed on nine-by-twelve paper, with quarter inch squares. If the graph is too small, you just might put the temperature point in the wrong place, or lose a day somewhere. Needless to say, that isn't recommended. Remember, we are trying to avoid confusion! Devote an entire page to each cycle. Don't try to skimp on paper. (Buy your own notebook).

While milady will be taking her temperature, tape testing and so forth, and dutifully reporting it, as a good wife should, his lordship should be keeping the charts.

The monthly charts should be made up, ready for entries, during the menstrual period. Number the days of each month, number the cycle days, "x" the menstrual days, and draw a heavy line down the chart from top to bottom, separating the first day of abstinence from the first part of the chart. You have already decided on the first day of abstinence. That is the day that allows you safety for your shortest possible period.

Your lordship, draw that line. Do it now. Remember, sir, you have drawn that line, yourself. Do not cross it, not if you intend to be a serious practitioner of rhythm.

As to the actual temperature taking, there is a lot to be said for taking it rectally, at that hour of the morning. One can even fall back to sleep.

Whatever method is used, it must be consistently the same each morning, and must be done before food or liquid intake or physical activity. The wife can keep a small dated notebook on her bedside table to mark the temperature reading in, as soon as she reads it. Then the husband can make his chart from this.

If both are in the habit of writing it down somewhere, there will be less chance of being tripped up by forgetfulness. Of course, the wife must report on the beginning and end of her menstrual periods for the chart.

This proprietorship of the chart by the husband is an absolutely essential element in promoting success, but we admit it can result in an oddity or two. For instance, it happens frequently in our family that milady finds herself asking his lordship when her next period is expected to start, and he tells her, right to the day.

That's all right. When you get to this point, you're on the right track.

* * *

Now, let's orient ourselves. The X's on the charts indicate menstruation. The dates are at the top of the chart. The numbers at the bottom indicate the days of the cycle. The circles indicate the last day of intercourse before the fertile time, and the first day of intercourse after the fertile time.

The basal thermometer calibrates from 96 to 100 degrees, in tenths of a degree, to record the relatively minute temperature changes. These degress are indicated at the left of the chart.

Until very recently, it was our habit to start the temperature on about the ninth or tenth day of the cycle. In later charts, you will see we have begun the temperature-taking on the eighth day, in view of our shortening cycle, to get those six temperature points in the lower box.

We do not continue with the temperature taking after resuming relations, but for those just beginning to learn the method, it would be good to continue in order to see your entire graph.

The letter P on the charts indicates the pain that we associate with ovulation.

At first glance, the charts may appear quite incomprehensible to the untrained eye. We are reminded of the farmer—giving confusing and detailed instructions to the passing motorist as to how to reach his destination—who finally confesses, "You can't get there from here."

Well, you *can* get there from here. As with any objective, once it has been reached, the pathway behind is clear and obvious. It is our intention to teach you to read a great variety of charts, with all their inherent variables.

In doing this, we have not chosen selected simple charts. This would have simplified our teaching job, and your learning job, but it wouldn't have done you much good in learning to read your own highly individual charts.

We are giving herewith a chronological series of our own individual charts. There were times when we ourselves were confused. We shall point these out to you, for by observing the confusion that existed, and our retrospective understanding, you will be aided in your own understanding of these and other charts.

We suggest most strongly that you do not limit yourselves to one reading. Several readings, until understanding is achieved, are imperative.

In reading these charts, you will see that going by temperature alone one may be confused by a second rise, or false peak. For a long time, this prolonged our period of abstinence, and delayed unnecessarily our resumption of sexual relations. But in retrospectively applying the "windows", we have clarified the division between the two levels. Later charts will show how we have been able to resume marital relations with less unnecessary delay.

If we have erred in the practice of rhythm, it has been by being overcautious. We ask that you be not dismayed by the sometimes overlong abstinence in these early charts. Remain with us, and we believe that you will soon be ably interpreting your own charts.

Remember, as you read this, that we did not come across Dr. Holt's windows until the twelfth chart. The application of them to the previous charts was then used to demonstrate how they related.

Proceed now. The way is charted.

CHART NO. 1

This chart begins with temperature taking on the 9th day. The 11th day was missed for some unremembered reason. Temperature was resumed on the 12th day.

The dotted lines indicate the 12 to 16 days before menstruation (counting backwards from next period) during which ovulation could have occurred. In this chart, it was between the 13th and 17th cycle days, counting forward from last period.

The rise in temperature level is clear and obvious. It is followed by a slight dip and a second rise. It is this second rise that has always caused problems and difficulties in the interpretation of the charts.

Abstinence began on the 8th day, and was continued until, but not including, the 21st day. The pain that we associate with ovulation occurred on the 13th day.

Relations could have been safely resumed on the 18th day, since conception cannot occur during the eleven days before menstruation. Dr. Holt's theory indicates the 17th day as being at least twenty-four hours after ovulation. (Three temperature points in the second box).

We abstained until we were safe for a 31-day menstrual cycle. We had not yet learned the trick of lopping off days on the far side.

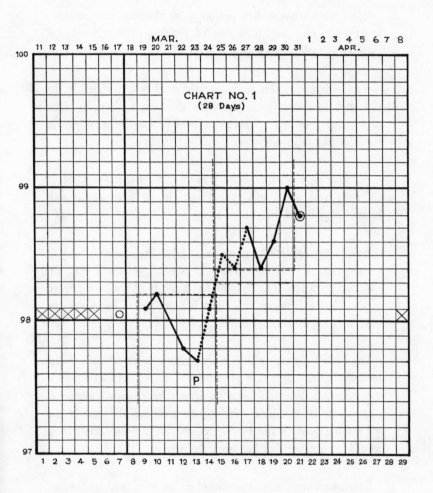

CHART NO. 2

Here we have a 30-day period, with the temperature start-ing on the 10th day. The area of possible ovulation was be-tween the 15th and 19th cycle days.

You will notice this fertile area started one day before the dip, and continued two days after the first high point. One of the major factors to recognize here is that the temperature rose ten points in one day.

Sometimes, as in this chart, there will be a sharp dip before the rise. And when you have a fast rise of this type, it will be included in the ovulatory area.

Following ovulation, there is a false dip, followed by a second rise. It was this false dip which prolonged our ab-stinence until the 25th day of the cycle. Had we been aware of Dr. Holt's theory at this time, it would have been obvious that the first dip and rise indicated ovulation.

Dr. Holt's theory indicates that relations could have been resumed on the 19th day of the cycle, or the 12th day before menstruation. You will note we do not have our six tempera-ture points in the first window, because we did not begin the temperature taking early enough. We are assuming they would fit, because that has been the pattern.

Because of our lack of knowledge, we abstained for seven-teen days. This was not easy. However, it didn't destroy our marriage. Nor did we get pregnant.

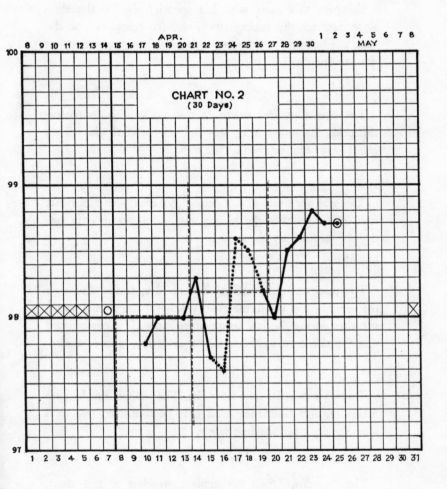

CHART NO. 3

Compare this chart with last month's. Notice the slow, slow rise, actually taking five days, (counting as one day each line between two temperature points), as opposed to one day last month.

The ovulatory area began at the dip, and ended before the peak. Relations were resumed on the 20th day. They could have been resumed on the 18th.

This was our usual 28-day period. We continued abstinence until two days after the high point, which meant only two days of unnecessary abstinence.

The pain was observed on the 14th day, or one day after the beginning of the fertile area. Whenever the pain is noted, it comes during the low temperature range. It is our opinion that the pain occurs either a day or so before, or at ovulation.

There are benefits to a slow rise. The peak is much more definitive, and abstinence must only be continued two days after the peak for absolute safety.

The "windows" will not apply themselves to this chart, because of the temperature point on the 19th day being too low.

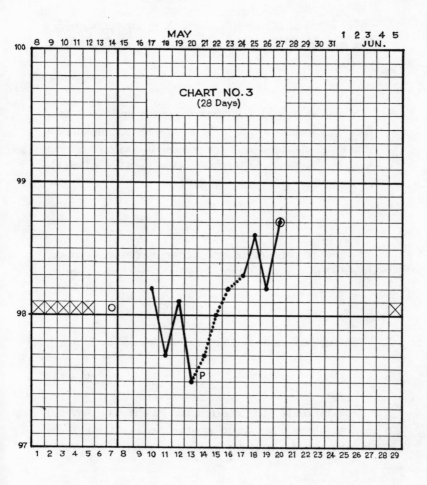

CHART NO. 4

This is one of our favorite charts. A 29-day period, with a clear rise, an obvious peak, and a beautiful leveling off.

(It may seem odd, but we always take pride in a good chart. It somehow seems to be a personal accomplishment. A husband should always compliment his wife on a good chart, just as he would for an excellent meal for which she has slaved over a hot stove all day).

Twelve days abstinence here, relations ceasing, as always, after the 7th day, and resuming in this case on the 20th day.

The pain occurs on the first day of possible ovulation.

Relations could have been resumed on the 19th day, with absolute safety. When we resumed relations on the 20th day, we were safe for a 31-day menstrual cycle.

Dr. Holt's theory applies nicely here.

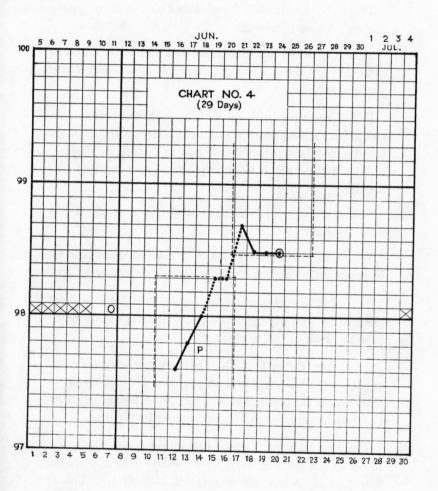

CHART NO. 5

This is the annual oddball period that we run into: 33 days, five days longer than usual.

This chart is unique in the four days of even temperature before the rise. Here we have an example of the value of the virtue of patience.

Following this lethargy on the part of the temperature, the rise is fast, achieving ten points in two days. Obviously, the five-day possibility of ovulation had to include one side of the rise or the other. It follows the peak, rather than precedes the rise.

The pain occurred on the day before the first day of possible ovulation.

We resumed relations on the 23rd day, at which time we were safe for a 33-day menstrual cycle, which is what we had.

The windows recommend safety two days before we felt safe, on the 13th day before menstruation. (Again, we didn't have Dr. Holt at that time).

This chart shows how Dr. Holt's system may offer the greatest hope for some time cutting into the taboo area, as other charts, in conjunction with the use of the fertility tape, (later to be demonstrated), show this to be accurate.

The tic-tac-toe game appearing in the lower right-hand corner of the chart occurred on Cycle Day No. 18, after the four days of unchanging temperature. Nobody won, but on the other hand, nobody lost, either. As you can see, we were pretty desperate for a little action.

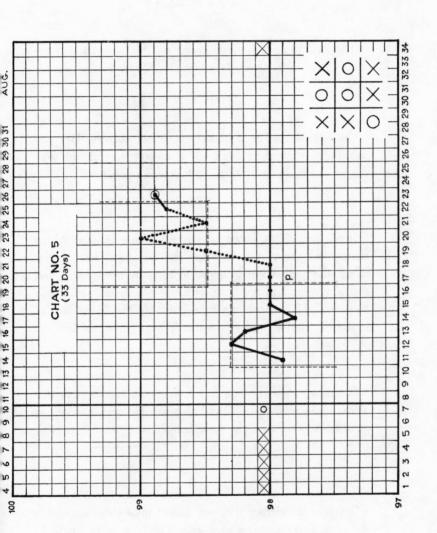

CHART NO. 6

The first thing you must notice on this chart is that the dotted lines cover seven days, not five. There is a reason for this.

On August 30, Helen underwent minor surgery. Her period started three days later. (The surgery was on the 25th day of the cycle, and therefore followed ovulation).

It is our opinion, based on our experience in reading the charts, and the perfect four-day rise contained herein, that this 27-day period was brought on early by the surgery, and that if surgery had not been performed, a 29-day period was most likely. Therefore, we have indicated the fertile area as it actually existed, and as we feel it would have existed.

Assuming a 29-day period, we were safe on the 19th day of the cycle, or one day after the peak. The windows are in accord with this, with the third temperature point also occurring on the 19th day.

If you're wondering why we waited until three days after the peak, following this slow rise, it is because hospitals do not have locks on their doors. Not even in private rooms.

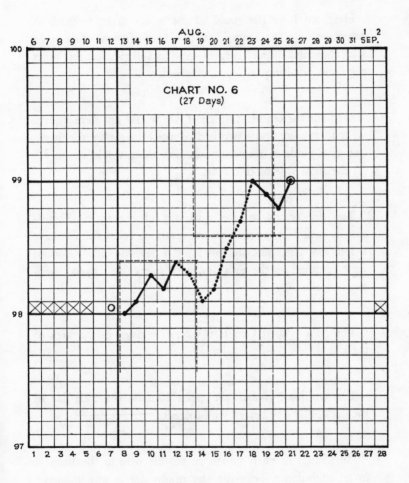

CHART NO. 6
(27 Days)

CHART NO. 7

Here we have the proof of the temperature method. A complication set in requiring a blood transfusion—there is no such thing as "minor" surgery—and as you can see, this upset the cycle, resulting in a 38-day period.

Without the temperature chart, we would not have known what to expect; and if we had counted days *after* menstruation as a guide to resuming relations, there would be no X's on the right side of this chart.

The dip occurs on the 23rd day of the cycle. This is usually well past the time we are resuming relations. We have a four-day rise, followed by a 2-day leveling off. Relations were resumed on the 29th day, with safety for a 39-day menstrual cycle.

The pain occurred on two successive days, at the area of the dip.

The windows give us the green light on the 28th day of the cycle, one day before we proceeded.

(Incidentally, when a man rushes his wife to the hospital in an ambulance, believing she might die at any moment, the balsa-wood cross of temporary abstinence seems very light indeed).

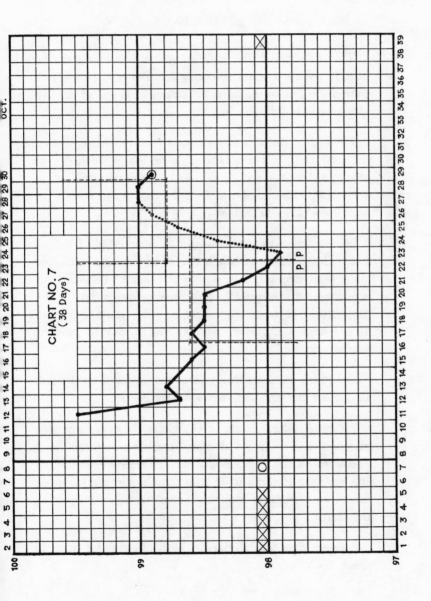

CHART NO. 7
(38 Days)

CHART NO. 8

This chart was a fooler. We have an apparent seven-day rise. In reality, it was a three-day rise. But we again weren't sure if the first or second peak indicated the end of the five-day possibility of ovulation.

Frequently, you will find a second peak following the first. In most cases, this is a false peak, and it is the first peak that indicates the end or near-end of the ovulatory phase. Generally, with a slow rise, it is the first peak. With a fast rise, it could be the second peak.

One variation to watch out for is what is called a "step rise." This consists of a number of small rises and levels, and these short interim levels, during the time of ovulation, are sometimes misinterpreted as the post-ovulation levels. Our Chart No. 9 is the closest we come to the classic "step rise." If one applies Dr. Holt, the step rise is easy to interpret correctly.

Dr. Holt's windows here give us the go-ahead on the 11th day before menstruation, on Cycle Day No. 17.

We were still not aware of Dr. Holt's theory, and because of that second peak, we abstained until we were safe for a 31-day menstrual cycle. Four days unnecessary abstinence. But we were learning more each month, and the following month we brought in additional factors to aid in interpreting the charts.

Fourteen days total abstinence. Difficult, yes. But peace of mind, it's wonderful.

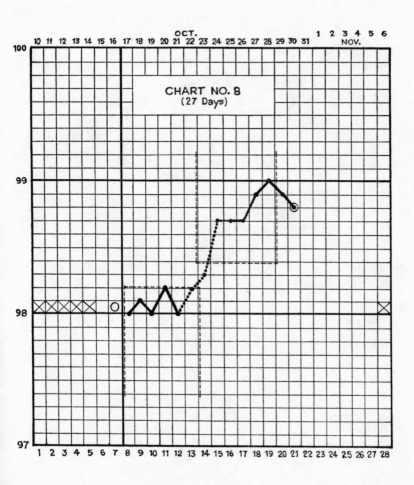

CHART NO. 8
(27 Days)

CHAPTER 7

YOUR LIPS ARE RED, YOUR TAPE IS BLUE, GLUCOSE IS SWEET, AND SO ARE YOU

The fertility tape, when used by itself or in conjunction with the basal thermometer, is an aid in pinpointing the time of ovulation after it has occurred.

At the time of ovulation, and just before and after, glucose is present at the cervix to aid the sperm in attaining longevity. The pink fertility tape, upon contact with this glucose, turns blue, to a greater or lesser extent.

Weston Laboratories, of Ottowa, Illinois, is the manufacturer of the tape. They also manufacture the Fertility Testor, with which to perform the test. Another device, the Rhythm Meter, manufactured by G&M Laboratories of Henderson, Kentucky, may also be used in this test.

We have said the fertility tape pinpoints ovulation after the fact. Unfortunately, it is not helpful at the beginning of the cycle. As you will see from the charts, we have obtained "blue" readings on each day from the end of menstruation to and including ovulation. This is because glucose is present in the menstrual fluid, and some remnants remain for several days after the cessation of bleeding.

Therefore, at the beginning of the cycle, you must still rely upon your knowledge of your minimum period. This in no way detracts from the usefulness of the tape. It is most satisfying to know, from the tape, that ovulation has occurred, and is done with.

We would not recommend the use of the tape without the basal temperature. The tape readings are sometimes erratic; but they are a part of the total picture, and contribute greatly to a clear understanding of ovulation. And what a godsend to those women who have "unreadable" charts!

The heaviest "blue" will usually occur at about the time of the lowest temperature point. As the temperature rises, the blue will diminish and disappear. After the temperature has risen, and the tape has stopped turning blue, and remains pink for three days, it is said you may safely resume relations.

In our various trials, we have encountered obstacles and difficulties—minor and not so minor—which the authors of the textbooks and instructional materials have not mentioned, or have failed to explain.

With any of these methods, there will be those who will apply them once, with complete success, then and forever after—a minority.

There will be those who will apply them once, with complete and dismal failure, and nevermore.

We feel that when confronted with small degree of success with these methods, a conservative application of perseverance may well surmount the obstacles. Our first encounters with the tape were something less than heartening. Even after being instructed by a Catholic gynecologist in its use, our first experience with a tape applicator was unsuccessful, and the entire process was discontinued. Later use of another applicator was successful. We believe persistence and patience rate high in assuring success with any method.

Again, it is easier to be persistent and patient together than singly. Here is where the husband and wife, together, should brainstorm as to the significance of their findings. The wife takes the temperature and tape readings, but the husband should be informed in every instance, to assist in their interpretation. If he is made keeper of the charts, you will have a nice system of check and counter-check.

There is also a super-sensitive tape, for those women who are unable to obtain readings with the regular tape.

You may get transient blue readings during the post-ovulatory "safe" phase. Don't panic. We don't know why we get them, but it does happen.

Oh, yes, one more thing. Make sure you have thoroughly washed your applicator free of residue of glucose each time, or you will just keep getting blue readings.

We feel that the tape has a place in helping to demarcate the post-ovulatory safe phase, and therefore has a definite value.

On the following charts, we have added additional code letters, in varying intensities, to indicate particular phenomena, and the degree to which they occurred.

CONDITION	INTENSE	MODERATE	SLIGHT	NEGLIGIBLE
Ovulation pain	P	$\underline{p}$	p	—p
Cervical mucus	M	$\underline{m}$	m	—m
Blue tape	B	$\underline{b}$	b	—b

CHART NO. 9

With this chart, we began our experiments with the fertility tape. However, let us first examine the temperature chart itself.

We have an agonizing ten-day rise. The first peak, on the 17th day, indicated the actual end of the ovulatory area, but the almost-uninterrupted, step-type rise confused us. The miserable temperature just kept going up. Still not aware of Dr. Holt's theory, we abstained until the 21st day, quite unnecessarily.

The pain occurred on the 13th cycle day, or the 15th day before menstruation.

The tape was first used on the 8th day. We obtained light blue (b) readings immediately. These became heavier on the 12th through 14th cycle days, (B), dropped back to a lighter blue on the 15th day, then disappeared.

According to Weston Laboratories, we could have resumed relations on the 18th day. This is obviously correct. Dr. Holt's windows also indicate safety on the 18th day.

It appears that with the use of the fertility tape, Dr. Holt's theory may be substantiated for the serious student of rhythm.

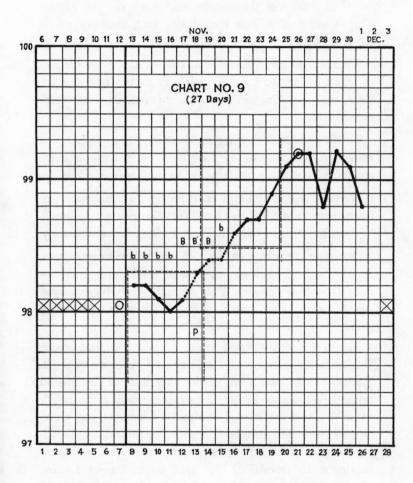

CHART NO. 9
(27 Days)

SEX, FERTILITY AND THE CATHOLIC

CHART NO. 10

On this chart, we have added an additional factor, a further "sign" of ovulation, the mucous discharge from the vagina. This occurred slightly on the 9th day (m), then heavier on the 10th (M).

We again obtained blue readings on the tape from the end of menstruation until the 12th day. From the 13th day onward, the tape remained pink. On the 13th day, the temperature rose.

On the 15th cycle day, we are three days past the last blue reading—which is recommended by Weston Labs—and we also have three temperature points in the upper window.

We were beginning to get excited about this combination of interpretive factors, but still couldn't believe our good fortune. We waited until the 19th day of the cycle, quite unnecessarily.

Ovulation *can* occur on the 12th day before menstruation. In this case, the windows and the tape would have us resuming relations on that day. They are most likely correct; even though, again, they intrude into the theoretical ovulatory phase.

This was a 26-day period, which we had never had before. Our extra abstinence at the beginning of the cycle paid off. Remember that this is one of the limitations of the rhythm method. We cannot yet forecast ovulation sufficiently in advance to signal the start of abstinence. Therefore, the beginning of abstinence must be arbitrarily determined, by abstaining for your shortest possible period, and possibly even subtracting a day from that. This must not be infringed upon.

The pain occurred slightly on the 11th day, then with more intensity on the 12th cycle day.

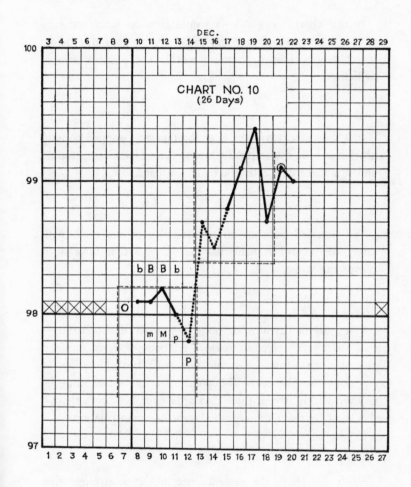

CHART NO. 11

In this chart, the windows would have us resuming relations on the 19th day of the cycle, or the 13th day before menstruation. This is obviously within the possible area of ovulation.

It is, however, two days after the tape has stopped turning blue; it is four days after the lowest point of the temperature, and it is three days after the ovulation pain.

We resumed relations on the 21st day of the cycle, with safety for a 31-day menstrual period, and that is what it turned out to be.

Our goal in rhythm has been to practice it successfully—that is, not conceive—to resume relations without unnecessary abstinence into the second safe area; and, if possible, to cut down abstinence to the point that intercourse may be enjoyed within two or three days after ovulation, even though this may be the 12th or 13th day before menstruation.

With this chart, the evidence becomes even stronger that the windows and the tape, used in conjunction with the temperature, will achieve that end.

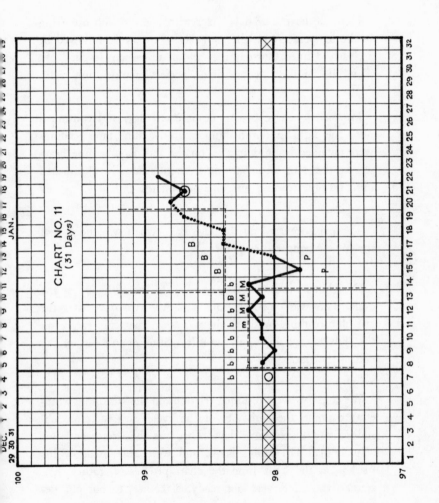

CHART NO. 11
(31 Days)

CHART NO. 12

Here we have a 28-day cycle, with a severe dip occurring in the temperature on the 14th day of the cycle, followed by a clearly defined four-day rise, and a subsequent leveling off. This falls in the category of a "perfect" temperature chart.

Mucous discharge began on the 10th day, and continued until the 14th, in diminishing quantity. Blue tape readings were obtained beginning, also, on the 10th day, became heavier on the 11th and 12th days, then gradually diminished until no blue reading was obtained on the 17th day.

The pain occurred on the 14th day, which was the day of the lowest temperature point.

Dr. Holt's windows give the okay to the 18th day of the cycle. This was obviously safe, and was two days after the last blue reading. Without the windows, the temperature on the 18th day would supply no information as to safety or the end of the rise.

We conservatively resumed relations on the 5th upper temperature point, the 20th day of the cycle, and therefore abstained two unnecessary days. This was the first month we actually had Dr. Holt's book, and were able to apply his method at the same time the chart progressed, rather than retroactively. We were not ready, of course, to put our dependence on the reliability of that third point; although we now see it was absolutely within the safe area.

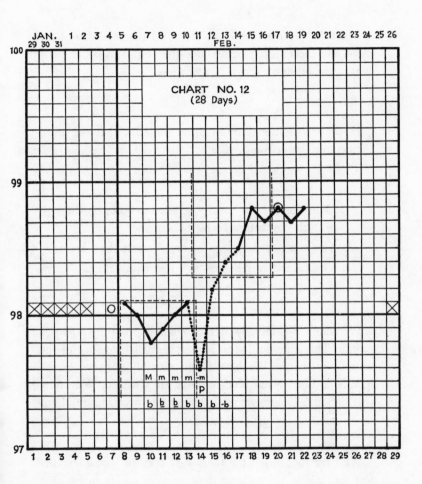

CHART NO. 13

The third temperature point occurs on the 22nd day of the cycle, and the 13th day before menstruation. This is definitely within the arbitrary range of ovulation.

However, additional information indicates that the third temperature point is indeed safe:

1. Ovulation is most usually believed to occur on the 14th or 15th day before menstruation.
2. The mucous discharge occurred seven days before.
3. The pain occurred four and five days before.

We obtained absolutely no blue readings from the tape this month. This may be due to having a smaller amount of the mucous discharge. We have found monthly variance in the quality of blue, when blue readings are obtained. We know that the tapes deteriorate with exposure to heat, light and air.

We have found that the tapes vary both in appearance before use, and in the color of the blue after use, from package to package. Here, again, experience with your reaction to the tape is your best gauge of what the tape is indicating.

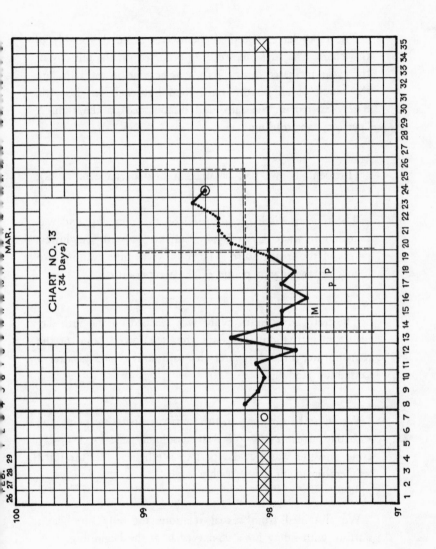

CHART NO. 14

The tapes have redeemed themselves quite thoroughly in this chart. The first blue reading occurred on the 9th day of the cycle, increased on the 10th, was heavier on the 11th, and the bluest of all on the 12th; then lightened on the 13th, barely existed on the 14th, and disappeared on the 15th. A "perfect" tape teading.

(Incidentally, we had obtained a new package of tapes).

The mucous discharge occurred on the 11th day, and was followed by two days of pain, concurrent with the lowest points of the temperature. The most vivid blue reading also occurs on the lowest points of the temperature.

The third temperature point was reached on the 12th day before menstruation, four days after the lowest point of the temperature, three days after the pain, and two days after a faint blue reading.

We resumed relations on the fourth temperature point, the 17th day of the cycle. We were absolutely safe for a 27-day cycle, and this was a 27-day period. We believe that the third temperature point was probably safe.

We abstained from sexual relations for only nine days, starting with safety for a 26-day cycle at the beginning.

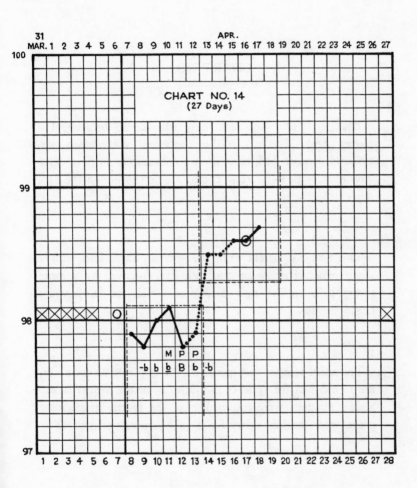

CHART NO. 14
(27 Days)

CHART NO. 15

Back to twelve days abstinence this month because of a 30-day period. The tape readings occurred without any particularly deep or dark blue, in two consecutive series of three days each, with a failure to obtain a blue reading on the 14th day of the cycle.

This was concurrent with the mucous flow, and with a slight pain occurring on the 14th day, followed by a more severe pain on the 15th day, after which the temperature began its rise.

The third temperature point in the upper level occurs on the 19th day of the cycle, or the 12th day before menstruation. Sexual relations were resumed as of the fourth temperature point, with absolute safety for a 32-day menstrual period.

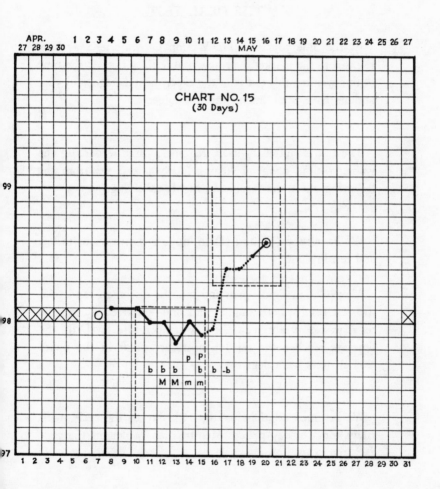

CHART NO. 15
(30 Days)

CHART NO. 16

THE ORAL TEST

By the time you read this, Weston Laboratories may have released to the market their new oral fertility test. At the time of this writing, this test is in the experimental stage, and your authors have been among the test subjects.

The test is simplicity itself, requiring three seconds of the woman's time upon awakening. As you can see from the following chart, the results are highly satisfying.

We have used (F) and (f) to indicate the reactions to this oral fertility test.

All ovulation signs—pain and mucous discharge—and positive test results, both vaginal and oral—occurred during the six days concurrent with the low temperature level. By the time we reached the third temperature point in the upper box, all tests were negative.

We resumed relations on the 17th day of the cycle, with safety for a 27-day period. Menstruation began on the 27th day, giving us a 26-day cycle.

The rhythm method of birth control just keeps getting easier all the time.

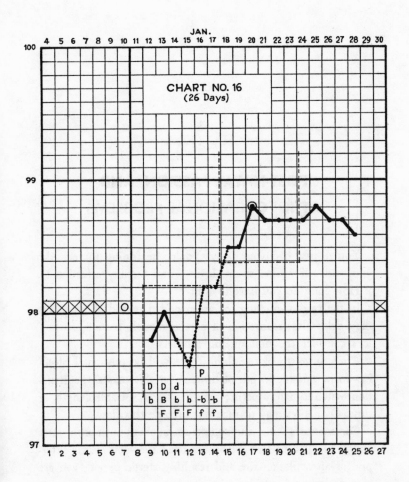

JAN.

CHART NO. 16
(26 Days)

CHAPTER 8

POST-NATAL PASSION, AND
OTHER OCCASIONAL PROBLEMS

You've just had your baby. You're beginning to feel like your old self again: sweet, loving, and terribly affectionate. How long do you have to wait?

In the case of nursing for an extended period of time, this may delay the resumption of a recognizable pattern, so first let's consider the non-nursing mothers.

After the birth of the child, there will be post-natal bleeding for a variable length of time. After this ceases, menstruation will ultimately occur; again, after a variable length of time. Ovulation may or may not precede this flow.

Commence taking the temperature about a month after childbirth. If a pattern establishes itself that you clearly interpret as an ovulation rise and resulting sterile period, you are in a position to consider using it.

However, we would suggest that unless you have become experts in interpreting your charts, you should observe a cycle before assuming that a pattern is established. Of course, we are speaking of abstinence running into a considerable length of time here.

This brings us to a somewhat ticklish point. After perhaps two months of abstinence or more, depending on pre-natal abstinence, the first recognizable menstrual period affords the first safe "island" for sexual relations. This first mensis will be followed by perhaps an erratic, undependable cycle, which may be terribly short or unbearably long. (Like forty-one days).

Regarding intercourse during the menses, not only after childbirth, but in the general practice of rhythm, Dr. Holt has said: "The dislike some people are supposed to feel with respect to the use of this sterile period seems surmountable. The idea that intercourse during menstruation is harmful we can safely relegate to the realm of fables."

Remember that an irregularly short cycle would bring the ovulation point much earlier in the cycle, so starting your abstinence right after the cessation of the menstrual flow would not be a bad idea for a while. At least give it a good margin over what you may have used previously. It may be that the cycle pattern is going to change somewhat from what it had been before childbirth.

Following is a chart showing the temperature pattern after birth. We did not start taking the temperature readings until the end of the first menstruation. It is better to start the temperature before this time, for the sake of observation. On this chart, although the cycle following the first recognizable menstruation is irregularly long, it produces a clear pattern of ovulation which assured us that stability had been re-sumed. Following this cycle, the pattern re-established itself within normal limits.

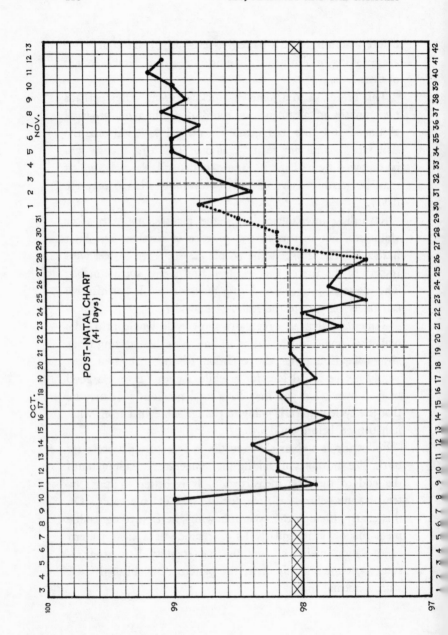

POST-NATAL CHART
(41 Days)

We had weathered the storm.

Retrospectively, it can be seen that had we been aware of Dr. Holt's theory prior to this time, it would have been very helpful in reading this chart.

*   *   *

For the nursing mother, resumption of the pattern will be delayed. It is generally considered quite possible that ovulation can occur during lactation. We have also heard it recommended by some as a means of spacing births.

As a means of preventing conception, therefore, we hear pro and con, but one point we may make is that at the time of weaning, one has to follow a procedure similar to that of the non-nursing mother's post-natal program. Some may wish to do this sooner, rather than later. We have heard that conception during the weaning period is quite common, so the practice of creative abstinence during the establishment of the cycle pattern is imperative.

If you have decided to nurse, you would do well to become particularly informed. There is an organization designed to help mothers nurse their babies: La Leche League International, Inc. They have literature to send to you upon request, and you should inquire specifically about information regarding breast feeding for spacing babies.

Remember, however, that their main purpose is successful breast feeding, not the spacing of births. The name La Leche, "the milk", is derived from an exquisitely beautiful Spanish title for Our Lady: *"Nuestra Senora de la Leche y Buen Parto"*—"Our Lady of Happy Delivery and Plentiful Milk." Their address is 9606 Franklin Avenue, Franklin Park, Illinois.

At one point, Dr. Holt describes the ups and downs of the temperature graph as "Tidal Waves of Temperature." Isn't that romantic? Very flattering to the female. Generates a sort of Mother Earth image. But what about the woman stranded on a becalmed sea?

For the woman entering menopause, or the exceptional woman who has some anovulatory (sterile) cycles, the pattern is more difficult to ascertain, but it is there.

Here again, careful records of past performance are important. Until such records are sufficient to indicate the irregular pattern, you are going to have to exercise extreme caution. It would appear that science will soon have something helpful to offer to this woman. So hold on, old girl.

At any rate, this woman and her husband should observe all the normal charts she has; that is, those which clearly show the "Tidal Wave" of ovulation. Then, when she has a chart which does not show a rise, (but has not been interfered with by ill health, an operation, etc.), this would indicate abstaining for a longer period than usual.

Dr. Holt suggests adding two or three days to the cycle day which has heretofore been the latest cycle day that you have abstained. He considers that you are thereby giving the "Tidal Wave" ample time to show up, if it is going to.

And, of course, if it isn't going to, you are having a sterile period, and you needn't have been abstaining all that time, anyway, more's the pity. But never mind that, at this point you aren't abstaining any more, anyway, so why fret?

It is when considering these particular difficulties and peculiar hardships that we are especially grateful for the dedicated men and women of Weston Laboratories, and remind you that the tests they have devised, both oral and vaginal, could be most helpful.

All this would apply to a woman who has some history of anovulatory cycles, and usually irregular menstruation. If a woman appeared to be having the first sterile cycle in her history, don't you think it might be well to sit pat on that one?

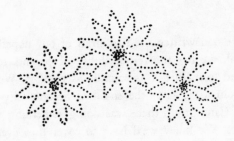

CHAPTER 9

ONE BED, TWO AIRPLANES

After we had written the first draft of our hopefully help-ful journal, we felt the responsibility of parents towards it and desired to mature it as roundly as possible. We live not too far from a big city—the so-called Second City—and we knew the Cana group there was doing something with rhy-thm clinics. We knew we'd have to cover this, even though we don't get into the Big City very often. (Our out-of-state relatives make it much more frequently).

At this point a golden opportunity presented itself, super-ceding the trip to Chicago. We found it little more difficult to fly to Washington, D.C., to attend the First International Symposium on Rhythm, sponsored by the Family Life Bureau of the National Catholic Welfare Conference and the Na-tional Federation of Catholic Physicians' Guilds. Obviously, this would be the last word.

It has been our misfortune, on each and every rare occasion that we have been away from home for a night, to find our-

ONE BED, TWO AIRPLANES   123

selves abstaining; and this trip promised to be no exception.
Sure enough, the day we arrived in the Capitol proved to be
our first day of abstinence.

We flew in two hours apart, on separate planes. This was
a result of a solid conservative upbringing, resulting in the
philosophy that four daughters with one parent are better off
than four daughters with no parents at all.

The flights were marvelous and trouble-free, although your
highly impressionable female author did find herself, at take-
off, reading about a plane crash, no survivors.

Your male author had two priests on his flight—although
at the time he assumed they were Catholic, he realizes in
retrospect they could just as easily have been Episcopalian—
and he felt assured that should anything go awry, he would
be well taken care of in the area of the last rites.

We love to fly—after all, it's the *only* way to travel—but
we are not blase enough to neglect those important Hail
Marys.

We made the mistake of mentioning our separate travel
arrangements to a young doctor and his wife at the Symposium, who we had discovered were of the anti-abstinence
camp. They were amused and somewhat contemptuous of our
conservative attitude toward modern travel—and, we inferred,
toward theology.

Well, all we can say is that while we flew in separate
planes, we slept in the same bed. And considering the alone-
togetherness, the exciting environment, and the glamorous
surroundings at the hotel, it just goes to show that abstinence is never impossible.

Don't these people who object to abstinence get any satisfaction at all from kisses?

There were over two hundred assembled, mostly priests

and doctors, a handful of nuns and an assortment of lay men and women. They had come because they were vitally concerned, and were seeking information and cooperation. Certainly no one could charge these priests with indifference to the problems of the married laity. They carry a painful burden of responsibility.

Sometimes when we hear someone generalize smugly about "priests," we are reminded of G. K. Chesterton's indignation when confronted with the popular stereotyped image of the clergy of his time. The priests at the Symposium could not be pigeonholed, and they made superfluous the question asked in print recently, "Can a Priest be a Modern Man?"

Detractors of the traditional theological position will say "celibate clergy" as if with this term they emasculated them en masse. We found that if any generalization were to be made about this group of priests it would be that they were outstandingly dynamic and virile, with a lively awareness of the world around them.

The keynote speaker, representing the Catholic doctors, was Dr. John Marshall of London, England. Our prior acquaintance with the work of Dr. Marshall had been the volume, *"Medicine and Morals,"* a part of the 20th Century Encyclopedia of Catholicism. We had found this to be sensitively and beautifully written, with a reverence for truth and an impatience with those "scientists" who fail to be scientific.

This Catholic Englishman has great presence, and easily fits the image evoked by the reading of his work—humanity, humor and charm.

We have previously touched on Dr. Marshall's book, "The Infertile Period," published by Helicon Press, Baltimore. It is an invaluable book for layman or doctor. As medical advisor to the Catholic Marriage Advisory Council of England,

Dr. Marshall covers the psychological and theological aspects with a competence few men are in a position to achieve.

The Symposium was an experience, in more ways than one. In four ways, to be exact:

THE BUFFALO EXPERIENCE

The Buffalo Family Clinic has served more than eight hundred couples since it began in 1961. Rev. Dino J. Lorenzetti and Dr. Joseph Ricotta spoke of their work and methods with fervent pride and enthusiasm. They have seen what a combination of the temperature chart, the vaginal tape and their hard work has accomplished—the hard work, that is, of twenty obstetricians and priests, working as teams, donating their time to the five-day-a-week clinic.

They have been technically successful, with an effectiveness surpassing eighty-eight per cent—including the "dropouts"—and they stress the meaning of Christian marriage, along with the technical knowledge, in their consultations.

THE CHICAGO EXPERIENCE

Under the direction of the Rev. Walter Imbiorski, Director of the Cana Conference of Chicago, the Catholic Family Information Service has set up a program involving the use of twelve centers, each of which holds a session every other month. These are two-hour sessions run by trained teams—priest, doctor and married couple.

The Chicago group unquestionably attracted the most attention with the Avis "We Try Harder" buttons which each of them wore, especially the leader couple who had misinterpreted a "step rise" in their chart and were now obviously pregnant.

Maybe they didn't know about Dr. Holt.

The report of their work was accompanied by a folder of literature which speaks for a highly organized, superbly balanced program, befitting the important Archdiocese it serves. We found this group had arrived at a number of the same conclusions we had. The results of their questionnaire to their "customers" were extremely interesting.

Among the many responses their questionnaire evoked, there were comments that—aside from the help obtained in understanding family planning—these conferences helped to remind and impress the couples with their duty of charity and understanding toward one another. In this way, these sessions might almost serve as group therapy in marriage counseling, and help these couples to clarify for themselves not only where they stand in the scale of progress, but where they plan to go.

The reaction these couples displayed, and the jointness or separateness thereof, might serve as an index to their entire marital approach.

Under technical complaints we noted that quite a few complained of being too irregular. Where this complaint appears, it is certainly understandable, because it is experience and familiarity with one's own patterns which are the most effective tools, and this comes about by patience and an inquisitive perseverance.

The claims of irregularity are not a valid reason for failure if one pursues the rules for irregularity, to determine the pattern. Unfortunately, doctors who have studied thousands of cases in clinics are more aware of this astounding trend to pattern than the general practitioner who reads an occa-

sional chart, but the latter is the one upon whom most us
us rely.

It must certainly be concluded that when a couple decide
they are a "problem" case, chart-wise, they could use a well-
informed doctor to lean on. There is the justified complaint
that these well-informed doctors are few and far between.
A data-clearing house, which was mentioned later in the
Symposium, would be very helpful to the average doctor
trying to assist in interpreting a chart.

The unfavorable comments noted in the Chicago Experience were less than half, but we're sure the Cana people are
more than half concerned with them.

We hope we are understood to be objective in addressing
these, and not impugned for lack of charity or sympathy.
Most of the claims of failure on a technicality were a result
of too little information.

Another unfortunate anomaly manifest in the unfavorable
comments is that a failure with the rhythm method seems to
engender a fury of panic and bitterness in couples which
bears no resemblance to a similar failure with, say, a condom.
This is probably attributable to an anticipation of continuing
failure, associated unjustly with the one and not the other.

The more we look into the technical aspects of rhythm,
the more convinced we become that technical failures should
be very low.

But—aha!—the human critter is bound to set up a psychological obstacle course. If we could just separate the groups
into (1) not able to understand and/or apply the method,
and (2) not able to abstain, we could work on the problems
nicely.

But the people who resent abstaining—only because they
cannot express their love, of course, and not because of any

personal inconvenience—keep insisting it won't work technically. And the people who have failed to understand the mechanics of it tend to clothe their confusion with a cloak of libidinous lack of restraint. This makes for an infinite variety of special problems for the experts.

One male commented, very indignantly, that he "went off rhythm just one night," and his wife got pregnant. He goes on: "When a husband and wife put up with the trials of life and family, I think the least they should be able to do is love one another whenever they want to. Things are tough enough without abstaining."

Apparently this man felt that sex was the pay-check for being married and having a family. What can one say to this "The world owes me a living" attitude which must see the material reward for every sacrifice or difficulty dangling like a carrot before the horse?

This man will claim rhythm doesn't work, but he hasn't used it. What night did he pick to go "off rhythm"? That's right. The night his wife ovulated. And why did he go off rhythm? Because he wanted to "make love," and never mind the consequences.

Incidentally, "making love" is a strange euphemism, isn't it? To make or create love between human beings has so little to do with sexual gratification that it seems probable this very mistaken idea of "making love" may well be the villain in countless marriages.

THE MONTREAL EXPERIENCE

A group of Canadian families in Montreal has established a movement which is rapidly expanding there. Called *Serena*, it is an organization of Catholic couples practicing and studying rhythm, contributing to the growing body of information on the subject, and dispensing information and assistance to those who are interested. They have progressed to public lectures, and have assisted over four thousand couples, being careful always to preserve the spiritual integrity of their approach.

The founding couple, Mr. and Mrs. Gilles Breault, who single-handedly started this work in Canada—probably as a result of the "never-say-die" spirit of the French—were an inspiration.

They had a goodly amount of printed material, most of it in French. We optimistically obtained this literature, thinking we could puzzle through it, but we have now decided we won't stick our necks out that far. Our erudite parish theologian blithely informs us that "every civilized man speaks and reads French." So we are somewhat put in our places.

We think he probably resents us as emerging laymen.

We were a little wistful to see Dr. Marshall conversing away in French with the Montreal group. Those Englishmen are so continental.

The Montreal group is expanding so rapidly they cannot train couples fast enough to meet the demand. They call theirs the Sympto-Thermic method, because besides the temperature they emphasize seeking out individual ovulation symptoms. They place reliance on Dr. Holt, but in the short time for questions we had no opportunity to gauge their evaluation of his method.

THE MAURITIUS EXPERIENCE

For exotic flavor, this one beat them all. The speaker, Dr. W. M. O. Moore of London, quickly informed his audience that he might have considerable difficulty speaking in English, since he was actually an Irishman.

He was just the one for Walt Disney to use in one of his charming tales, should he need a fey young Irish doctor. The British Socialists had sent Dr. Moore to Mauritius, an island in the Indian Ocean which had a considerable population problem, due to a sharp drop in the infant and adult mortality rate from malaria. The ethnic groups on the island are highly diverse, and it became evident that the only birth regulation program acceptable to all was a rhythm clinic. The oriental people, particularly the Muslims, show a decided resistance to contraceptives.

With the cooperation of all the religious groups on the island, the clinic was established, and although the program is very new, the outstanding feature was that after training a reliable group of native instructors, they found they were able to instruct even illiterate husbands and wives in the basal temperature method.

It is, after all, very simple.

*   *   *

The doctors at the Symposium were in general agreement that the temperature method was most efficient, although some doctors did hold the position that the calendar method was perfectly satisfactory.

It was quite clear that in most cases a sacrifice of time and income was willingly undertaken by these men. Contraceptives are big business, but rhythm counseling reaps no monetary harvest. One doctor who spoke from the floor admitted it was very difficult to take time from his other work, but since he was the only Catholic doctor in his area, he had undertaken a rhythm clinic single-handed. Not many worried Catholic couples have had the good fortune to encounter a man like this.

Other doctors stated they were eager to implement the work in their own area, and that there was a need for a concerted effort, probably in the form of a national clearing house for data. Dr. Clement P. Cunningham, President of the Guilds, voiced his intention to push this forward.

In general discussion, it was set forth that as nearly as any estimate can be made, it appeared that the number of acts of intercourse per given month did not vary between couples using rhythm and couples using contraceptives. We think we won't speculate on this in print, but we're sure the reader will find some material for imaginative speculation here.

As for the "pill", there was discussion of the medical validity and effectiveness of its use in an attempt to regulate irregular cycles. It was pretty well agreed that the pill effects a regular cycle for only a limited time, perhaps up to six months after cessation of medication. If a couple is allowing only for the perfected cycle, they usually conceive the first month it reverts to its previous pattern.

Some doctors were so disgusted they wanted to leave the pill entirely alone. Others thought they would continue with regulation and treatment with the pill until the returns were all in.

Several doctors objected to the use of the pill by Catholics as a "back door to contraception," and many agreed wholeheartedly with Dr. Herbert Ratner's terrifying description of what the pill actually does to the woman who takes it.

For those with a strong stomach, the pamphlet by Dr. Ratner, Director of Public Health, Oak Park, Illinois, can be obtained from the Family Life Bureau of the NCWC, Washington, D.C.

So many different claims have been made about the pill in so many different places, we don't intend to give a recap on all available information. However, some doctors at the Symposium were convinced of its triple-threat action: that it either prevents ovulation or fails to prevent ovulation; that if it fails to prevent ovulation, it does one of two things: it produces a substance in the cervical mucus that acts as a diaphragm-type contraceptive; or if fertilization does occur, the ovum is unable to attach to the womb and is aborted.

One young doctor quoted the manufacturer of the pill as saying it produces a state like natural pregnancy, but he said, "I have never in my life seen anything in nature that resembles the lining of the womb of a woman on the pill."

Your authors' knowledge of the effects of the pill is derived only from reading and hearsay. (We toyed with the idea of taking it at one time to achieve the "perfect" cycle some theologians say we are entitled to, in order to report more authoritatively on its effects in this book, but after thoroughly researching it, we chickened out).

The greater part of the hearsay, from women who have taken it, is unfavorable. Some of them taking it for therapeutic purposes are living for the day when their doctors take them off it. The doctors, however, do not consider the pill a failure for these women—after all, they're still alive, and they're not pregnant—and will report them as successfully taking the pill. These women—and there is no way to gauge their number—will still have to rely on another means after their cycle has been "perfected."

The climax of the Symposium was reached when Father John Ford, S.J., of "Ford and Kelly" fame, professor of moral theology at the Catholic University of America—"the sanest man on marriage in America today"—spoke on the morality of periodic continence.

This big man, with iron gray hair and resonant voice, is almost more than one can hope for. He is deeply involved in the theological aspects of the moral problems inherent in family planning, and has obviously been all over the territory and back again many times.

A violent argument had arisen on the floor between two doctors regarding the morality of the pill. As the dispute reached the personal insult stage, Father Ford, in the truest ecumenical spirit, took control of the situation with this eloquent plea:

"With regard to these big arguments that are going on in the Church today, I think it is most important that we recognize with full charity the sincerity of people with whom we disagree.

"I disagree thoroughly, for instance, with what Canon Jannsens says, and I went to Canon Jannsens in his home in Louvain and talked the whole thing over with him.

"I have great respect for Canon Jannsens. Now, I think that anybody who feels as strongly as I do on this subject would be likely to be annoyed at certain things he hears.

"But have I made any remarks to that effect? Have I ever expressed any annoyance? Have I ever been tempted, or even called anybody by an improper name because of his theological views?

"Well, you'll know about that on Judgment Day."

CHAPTER 10

THE CORNERS OF CONSCIENCE

"Catholics should have at least as much religious freedom as those outside the Church. To be concrete: an American Catholic should be as free as a Catholic as he is as an American."

—James O'Gara, writing in *Commonweal*.[1]

In this one statement, Mr. O'Gara has enunciated the political premise upon which the extremists in our Church wish to base their "new theology."

There is no question that the Catholic Church in America has been strongly influenced by the political climate in which it exists. As a result, American Catholics have tended to equate "Freedom of Religion"—a *political* philosophy—with the *theological* premise of "Freedom of Conscience"—which by definition is meant to include a rightly-ordered and well-informed conscience.

Bishop James E. Kearney of Rochester, in a pastoral letter,

1 Oct. 16, 1964, p. 87.

warned that "Extreme ecumenical writers ask us to soften the concept of heresy. Extreme modern theologians ask us to soften the concept of sin."

The extremists are not content with the "open windows" of John XXIII. They breathe a distant air, touched with madness; and they insist that we "move out of our churches and abandon the great institutional structure which weighs us down."

They object to the concept of sacrifice upon which the Catholic Church is built, and they demand to know what right a celibate clergy has to say to them, "Thou shalt not."

They say to the celibate theologians, "You do not know marriage," and attempt to convince them that the sexual elementals of personal desire, personal pleasure and personal gratification do not exist in marriage, and that through marriage sex is transformed, in its totality, into a means of communication.

We do not deny that a good sexual relationship brings a man and woman closer together. But this is only a part of the totality of sex, and their pretense that marriage has lifted them above individual sexuality can only be described as a massive fraud which they are attempting to perpetrate upon the Church.

What enrages us most is their blatant insistence that rhythm doesn't work. And to prove it, they give us examples of people who have violated every rule of the practice of rhythm. Sadly enough, many who think they have failed with rhythm have never actually used rhythm at all, and they will unfortunately identify with an imaginary couple set up as straw men in one book, who:

Keep no records, do not use the temperature method, fearfully examine a small desk calendar *after* intercourse, and carelessly, with apparent intent, promote erotic situations which lead them into intercourse, pregnancy after pregnancy after pregnancy. But what else can they do? These writers deny the existence of any expression of love other than sexual intercourse.

In *"The Vine and the Olive,"*[1] a fictionized account of the failures of the rhythm method, Margaret Culkin Banning gives us the following characters:

"Remarkably fertile mother"; the city's "leading gynecologist," who knows nothing about the practice of rhythm; an ineffectual, faceless husband who plays no part in the responsibility of abstinence; a handful of "stupid Irish priests," and a group of intelligent, well-informed and articulate non-Catholic advocates of contraception, all of whom get the best lines.

In *"Contraception and Holiness,"*[2] Rosemary Ruether—who emphatically proclaims that sexual desire has no relevancy for her now that her husband has gone away to India for a year—gives us a defective lunar stopwatch that flashes red and green, and something horrible falling on us if we open the refrigerator door.

We suggest that Conscience can be a breeze or a hurricane, and like the wind, ever-shifting. And in the name of Sanity, we offer these words attributed to a nameless Indian:

"Conscience is a three-cornered thing in my heart that stands still when I am good, but when I am bad, it turns around and the corners hurt a lot. If I keep on doing wrong, the corners wear off and it does not hurt any more."

We'd like to have that Indian at the next Vatican Council.

1 Harper and Row, 1964.
2 Herder and Herder, 1964, pp. 86, 91.

CHAPTER 11

THE LION PIT

We undertook this book because we felt it was time for a free exchange of ideas among Catholic laymen regarding a subject widely misunderstood, and in some instances viewed with a stereotyped prejudice. The Catholic layman is being called upon to take, must take and is taking more responsibility in Catholic action.

Contrary to the apparent opinions of some of the more wild-eyed emerging laymen, this responsibility does not include the right to determine the moral teaching of the Church by popular vote.

As you can see from the preceding exposition, we don't know all the answers. We do know that we have made rhythm work for us, and that due to varying factors, it has failed for some Catholics. We feel this failure is bad for the morals, morale and public image of the Catholic family.

We cannot stress strongly enough that we are not advocating the practice of family limitation, per se, for Catholics. We are advocating the success of rhythm where it is practiced.

We are convinced from personal knowledge of the experiences of many good Catholic couples that this failure is not due to lack of self control, but to a factor more subtle than ignorance . . . a misunderstanding of the techniques involved in the successful practice of rhythm.

Obviously, one failure in this technique disqualifies one from any success for a good period of time.

Pope Pius XII has expressed the hope that science would find a way to render more secure the method of periodic continence, and it is apparent that whatever its refinements, periodic continence will always be the only morally acceptable fertility control available to Catholics.

The Revs. John Ford, S.J., and Gerald Kelly, S.J., writing in *The Catholic World,* stated:

"The Church is completely committed to the doctrine that contraception is intrinsically and gravely immoral and no substantial change in this teaching is possible. It is irrevocable."

Dr. John Rock, popular advocate of "the Pill", which he erroneously believed would be morally acceptable to Catholics, stated on one occasion that he is going beyond the pill, and is researching a method of forecasting ovulation sufficiently in advance to be a reliable signal.

While everybody has leaped upon Dr. Rock's pill, they seem to be ignoring his statement that if sufficient funds and concentration of research were focused on the problem, existing laboratory techniques could be perfected and simplified so that the average woman, in the privacy of her bedroom or bathroom, could easily and safely forecast and pinpoint ovulation.

What is generally overlooked by the harried layman is that only very recently have competent and diligent technicians, in increasing numbers, applied themselves to solving and clarifying what has been looked upon heretofore as a private problem. Harassed, conservative churchmen keep protesting that the whole contraceptive controversy could soon be made obsolete, but so loud are the voices of the rabble-rousers that these other voices are barely heard.

The statement of Leon Joseph Cardinal Suenens, Belgian Archbishop, that "a pill" will soon be perfected to allow family planning, with the approval of the Church, has been waved like a flag of approval for sterilization, and treated in the press like a coming reversal of the Church's position on contraception; when, in fact, what the Cardinal was obviously referring to is not the already-existing pill which prevents ovulation, but a pill not yet fully developed which will stimulate ovulation, and as such would be totally acceptable to Catholics. A pill of this type is now being tested by Upjohn.

Father John O'Brien, whom we mentioned in our Preface, has indicated that such a procedure—a method whereby ovulation could be precipitated with unerring regularity, which would expedite rather than frustrate a natural bodily function —would be morally acceptable to Catholics.

Research is now being conducted at St. Francis Hospital in Evanston, Illinois, to come up with a test which will forecast ovulation sufficiently in advance, and Georgetown University's Center for Population Research is conducting a nationwide study to help perfect the rhythm method.

The newest product to pinpoint ovulation is "Estrindex," manufactured by Colab Laboratories of Chicago Heights, Illinois. It is based on the concentrations of salt in a woman's body which increase prior to and at the time of ovulation. The test results have proved one hundred per cent effective.

An organization similar to *Serena* has become active in France. Results have been so good that some leading non-

Catholic gynecologists, who previously beat the drum for contraception, have joined their group, and now proclaim the superior efficacy of the rhythm method.

In the next few years, there is going to be a great leap forward, with resultant tremendous clarification, on the whole subject of rhythm. If we Catholics show ourselves loyal and receptive to the "conservative" approach, then all those publications so eager to exploit any controversial subject to gain readership will be forced to begin exploring the other side of the story.

When a writer strikes out with conviction and strong opinion on a controversial subject, he is bound to wind up with a "bias" or slant. If it is his own bias or slant, he has more right to be heard with open-minded consideration than the man who writes simply to capitalize on the bias or slant of others.

By the latter, we are referring to the plethora of "me too" editorials and features screaming about Catholics and birth control. Add to that the "out of context" reporting which peppers every major newspaper to achieve shock impact, and you have created an intolerable aura of tension.

The most flagrant example of this was a question in one of the Sunday supplements: "Is the Catholic Church going to approve oral contraceptives?" If you think they quoted the Pope, or a moral theologian, in their reply, guess again. They quoted Dr. Rock.

We are extremely vulnerable to this pre-digested reporting because our lives are so multifaceted that we cannot go to the source to be informed about all major questions of the day.

Our people who may be swept along in the precipitate current of those loudest voices of discord are unwittingly endangering their most precious heritage, the Church of

Christ. Perhaps they do not realize how many enemies she has, and how influential and active these enemies are.

For example, when International Communism looks at an objective, its first aim is the destruction of the Church; or, better yet, the re-forming of it to its own ends. The Communists use every tool, such as the increasing number of agnostics—and agnostic "Christians"—who feel that their own interests are encumbered by those with religious affiliations to whom expediency is not the only consideration.

When a religious man puts his convictions to practice, he gets in the way of those whose goals are simply materialistic. Our society is very largely materialistic, and we are set upon by those who would divide and conquer. Let's not allow ourselves to be panicked and stampeded.

It is a strange distortion of the Christian message that we hear voiced by some Catholics today. There are those who do believe that they are mortally sinning by their practice of contraception, but just figure they will "have" to continue to sin until the time when they hope the Church will change on this matter, and they won't "have" to sin any more.

Even supposing their shaky premise of change had validity, they do not perceive how they damage the spiritual fabric of their lives by continuous, deliberate sin. Apparently they actually believe that the filthy tattered remnants of their souls will be transfigured to beautiful, shimmering purity by a change of position on the part of the Church, and that the daily weaving—or rending—of the fabric bears no relationship to what it will become.

The Catholic Church is not alone in its stand on contraception. The Eastern Orthodox Churches have stated a similar position. Furthermore, although the publicly-stated

Protestant position is approval of contraception, there are many individuals among them who morally would feel more secure in the adoption of a rhythm technique in which they could place their confidence.

It is to be hoped that your sons and daughters will have available to them additional knowledge and methods which will make the proper practice of rhythm simpler and more efficacious for them, and that their success in rhythm, and their understanding of, and obedience to, the natural law of God, will obliterate forever this stumbling block to sanctity that exists in some Christian marriages.

In today's materialistic world, not only has sacrifice become old hat, but discipline is going out of the window, too. We'd be the last ones to masochistically cry out, "Let's all suffer!" But we are approaching in our society the dangerous ideal that equates suffering with disgrace.

Those who shed crocodile tears for contraception expect contraceptives to solve problems that they will not solve. They seem to be convinced that the use of contraceptives would give them a perfect love life. We suggest that perhaps their difficulty may lie elsewhere.

If a problem exists in child bearing and rearing that is great enough to cause such emotional turmoil, then it is great enough to exercise the caution of rhythm. But if abstinence itself is being blamed for greater turmoil, there usually exists a basic problem that is only aggravated by abstinence, not caused by it.

We have to agree with Playboy's editor when he says sex is beautiful. Strangely enough, what is not realized is that all the sex promoters rampant in the marketplace are utterly destroying sex, touching even those who rush to the marriage bed and pull the covers over their heads.

Sex has the unexpected stamina but inherent fragility of a lovely woman. The bigger-than-life reality the peddlers build up is towering above, shadowing, crushing the beautiful fragile reality, allowing it no sun and no quiet, cozy place to be nurtured. Very often a woman is made to feel that she has nothing to offer her sex-saturated husband but her availability.

These erotic images do become bigger than life, and have placed the wife in a continuous unreal rivalry with the shapely blonde stereotype presently in vogue. The male is invited to measure himself against the new "hero" who possesses an incredible appetite for sex, which an astonishing array of females are vying to satisfy. How much horseradish can you put on a roast beef sandwich, and still taste the meat?

It would be interesting to speculate, if given a choice of following a regime—for a period of a month or a year—of rigorously rationed calories or rigorously rationed sexual intercourse, how many people would face a great "moment of truth" regarding the matter of indulgence.

Do we stand alone in terrified contemplation of the imminent destruction of the foundation of our socio-spiritual structure? We speak of marriage, the holy union of man and woman, as decreed through God's natural order.

The Catholic Church sees the issue of contraception in this vaster setting. The Christian argument for the sanctity of marriage stands firmly on God's natural law, and by unlocking the gates to admit the stampede of contraception, what fences will be left standing to mark off the forbidden pastures?

Whether your children are in grade school, high school or college, are you not already facing the bitter social climate that is the aftermath of moral permissiveness? If you think

SEX, FERTILITY AND THE CATHOLIC

this inevitable result will not affect your children, you are deceiving yourself.

Is this the heritage we want to give our children? Absolute freedom, framed in social pressure and exalted by atrophied conscience, to choose the path of licentiousness? If we destroy the keystone of *holy* matrimony, then marriage can no longer stand.

We are sure that any Catholic who thinks he might favor contraception or sterilization believes this would not affect his attitude toward the sanctity of marriage. That might be. But he should not overlook the torrent of weak humanity that would sweep past him, upon the destruction of this vital lock, to inundate all barriers to divorce, adultery and free love.

We must never abandon the view that a good end never justifies the use of an intrinsically evil means. This is a hard law. Sometimes life is hard. Almost always, virtue is hard.

Each young Catholic, upon first reading of the early Christian martyrs, is inflamed with emotion, and silently asks himself: "What would I do if I had to make a choice?"

It is an intriguing question for any human to ask himself. "Am I capable of following my convictions to the grave?" We sadly suspect that there are some who would do better in the dramatic lion's pit than in the temporarily continent marital bed.

We Catholics stand today at the door to our bedroom. What will we embrace within that chamber?

Our Lady?

Or the tiger?